THE INCA TRAIL

Stories from Peru
Vivien Whitfield

Scripture Union

130 City Road, London EC1V 2NJ

© Vivien Whitfield 1989
First published 1989

ISBN 0 86201 518 9

Phototypeset by Input Typesetting Ltd., London
Printed and bound in Great Britain by
Cox and Wyman Ltd., Reading

Contents

The shepherd who became a sheep

Roberto picked up a stone and threw it as hard as he could. And another. It made him feel better. He wandered slowly off in the opposite direction, keeping up with the five sheep which were his to look after each day. He was ten now. For two years after his fourth birthday he'd had to help his father and the other men of the village by clearing the fields of stones, so that they could plough with their digging sticks. But day in, day out for the past four years he'd had to take care of the animals.

His eye caught a tiny movement on the ground beneath a nearby rock. A chinchilla played in the late afternoon sunshine. He was a plump little animal on short legs, with twitching whiskers, and his thick, brownish-grey fur contrasted with Roberto's ragged shirt. His large eyes and ears were constantly on the alert for danger; he was ready to nip back into the safety of the rock crevice should it be necessary. But Roberto was no danger.

Lucky thing, thought the boy. He can come and go as he likes. He's free to do what he wants. Not like me, tied to these sheep. He sighed a big sigh, and wished for the umpteenth time that he could be like Martin.

Martin was his cousin, and on his last visit from the big town he'd told a fascinated Roberto all about school, and reading and writing, and how he hoped to go to university, then find a job and earn lots of money. To Roberto, who'd never been further from the village than he was now, Martin was someone to admire indeed! His own father could read, but not many of the villagers could. Roberto wished he could go to school, but the nearest one was two hours' walk away, and besides, he was too useful looking after the animals.

The rays of the setting sun turned the chinchilla's grey fur to a dull red as Roberto called the sheep together. There was a sudden nip in the air, for they were 4,000 metres above sea level, and when the sun went down, the temperature usually dropped to freezing. He pulled on his chullo, his pointed woollen cap with earflaps to keep him warm. Then he wrapped his rough, brown alpaca-wool poncho around him, and headed for home.

Diana paused partway up the gentle slope that led to the little tin-roofed church. She wished she was a bit fitter. It was harder to get the oxygen she needed in the thin air so high up in the mountains, and she stood panting for breath, watching her companion bounding on upwards. Juana was a teenage girl from the church in the big town where Diana, the English woman, was working.

As she stood breathing in the thin, clear mountain air, Diana looked around her. All was very dry and barren on the shore of the Big Lake. It was hard to believe that there had ever been any floods. Diana's eyes rested on a few corrugated tin roofs below her, and then on the many mud roofs in the water itself. They were proof enough. The rains had come earlier in the year as usual, but they had gone on too long. The lake had risen and flooded the former village. How hard everyone had worked, rescuing the bewildered animals and beginning to rebuild, while they lived in white canvas tents loaned by the government. Now nearly all the tents had gone and people had their own huts again, of mud and straw or of corrugated tin.

All seemed peaceful and still as Diana continued her slow climb up to the new little church. She thought of why they had come. It was coming up to 28th July, Independence Day, when there would be two weeks school holiday. The church leaders had asked Diana to lead a Holiday Bible Club for the children for a few days, and now she and Juana were going to discuss it with the pastor. She wondered how many children would come.

Juana came running down the dry slope again, her worn skirt flying out behind her.

'There's no one here yet.' Her voice carried on the breeze and startled a big, black ibis bird, its long curving bill searching for food in the marshy edge of the lake. As it flew off, the sun glinted on its body, turning the dull black to a beautiful glossy green. 'Let's sit down and wait,' Juana continued. 'Look, there are some children over there with those llamas. I expect they'll come. Shall I go and tell them about it?'

'Perhaps we'd better check the dates with the church leaders, first, Juana. But that's a good idea. Let's pray now, and ask God to bring along all the children he wants to come.'

As they opened their eyes, there was a shout. 'Hola! Good afternoon! How are you? Welcome!' Two dark, stocky men, shorter than Diana, came striding effortlessly up the hillside. They shook hands with Diana and Juana and pointed to the church. 'Shall we go inside to talk?' They led the way, and Diana stooped to enter the low, dark doorway.

About thirty kilometres away, Roberto penned his sheep for the night in an enclosure next to the group of huts which was his home. He went into one of the huts to see if there was any soup left for him.

At least, he thought to himself, I could go away for a little while, if I could persuade David to help me.

David was his little brother, who – although he was six – had not yet been given responsibility with the animals. If he could persuade David to care for the sheep, Roberto could make himself scarce. Perhaps he could even reach the big town and find Martin?

One of his sisters saw him come in and went over to the big cooking pot on their pressed-mud stove. She threw some more of the dried llama dung used for fuel onto the fire, and stirred the contents of the pot. Then she filled a bowl and gave it to Roberto.

'It's chuño soup tonight,' she said. The flames lit up the blackened sun-baked mud and straw walls. The smell of the soup made Roberto hungrier than ever. He liked chuño, the special potato which was left outside on the frosty ground for three nights. What fun it had been to help trample on them all to squeeze out the moisture. Now they were black, and not at all like potatoes but they blended well with the rice, stock and few sticks of carrot that also went into the soup.

Roberto licked his lips. 'Thanks, Maria. I'm hungry!'

'Aren't we all?' his sister replied.

Another of Roberto's sisters – he had four altogether,

and three brothers, one of whom was a baby – was feeding the guinea-pigs with the carrot peelings. They squealed as they ran over the earth floor of the hut, in a variety of colours and sizes. On a shelf by the thatched roof were piles of cobs of yellow and purple maize, drying off amidst the smoke from the fire. Some would be made into a strong beer, the rest would be eaten over the next few months.

Roberto's mother squatted on her heels in a corner of the room, unslung the brightly-coloured woven shawl from her back, took out the baby and began feeding him. Gradually the rest of the family came inside, out of the growing darkness. Father and the older boys looked tired: they had worked hard clearing the last of the fields after the potato harvest. Father merely grunted when Maria brought him his soup. Roberto knew better than to ask permission for David to help him with the sheep, until his father had eaten and drunk.

There was no electricity where Roberto lived, only candles, so when the meal was over most of the family settled for the night, stretching out on a low platform at the end of the hut, close to each other for warmth. Roberto sighed again as he reached for an old sheepskin to lie on. Now that he'd made his plans, he felt unsure. But surely there was more to life than sitting on the high plains and looking after sheep?

As always at that time of year, the dawn broke crisp and blue. When the sun began to melt the frozen ground outside Roberto's hut, he was already up. He had fetched a bucket of water from the stream half a kilo-metre away, which was the family's only water supply. He filled his water bottle and grabbed a few bread rolls, putting them carefully into the folds of his poncho. He had had no difficulty at all in persuading David to help him care for the sheep that day. David was only too ready to feel grown-up. Their parents had made no objection either.

'Make sure they never stray out of your sight,' was his father's comment as they went out to collect the sheep from the pen.

As soon as they were out of earshot, Roberto turned to his brother. 'David, would you like to have the sheep all to yourself for a few days?'

'Why? Are you going away?'

'Yes, but Father might try to stop me, so it's got to be a secret. Can you keep a secret?'

David promised solemnly, his big brown eyes opening wider and wider as Roberto told him how he longed to get away and go to school, and how he was planning to go to the big town and try to find Martin.

'But what shall I say to Father when I come home without you? He's bound to notice!'

'Tell him I met a friend who invited me to celebrate Independence Day with his family. You can tell him I said you were good with the sheep. You know that's the most important thing. *We* don't matter so much. There are too many mouths to feed in our family already.'

David knew this was true, and it was unlikely there would be any trouble. He had the same kind of admiration for Roberto as Roberto had for Martin, so he excitedly agreed to it all.

The sheep were somewhat reluctant at first to stay with David, for they didn't know him too well, but they settled down to graze as their shepherd started back the way they had come. Once he reached the track which led towards the rough road to the big town,

Roberto turned off in that direction, the bleating of the sheep gradually becoming fainter and fainter.

Martin trudged home from school at lunch-time. Hooray! he thought. Holidays! The next day, 28th July, he was to join in the Independence March Past through the town. Already many people were arriving from other parts of the country to be with their families on this festive occasion when they celebrated the birth of their nation, independence from Spain. Already there were crowds in the main square, and lodging hostels were rapidly filling up.

As he turned into his street he almost collided with a tricycle carrying two women and a box of bananas. The mixed smell of fish and decaying rubbish reminded him that the market was round the corner. He coughed and spat in the dust as he came towards his house. A dog barked from the flat roof of the house opposite, and down the wide, pot-holed earth road rumbled a crowded bus. Four youths were hanging out of the door, holding onto whatever part of the doorway they were able to grab. Martin recognised one of them and shouted a greeting as the bus rolled past. His mother heard him and opened the door.

'Hola! Did you have a good day? Take your uniform off and I'll wash and iron it ready for tomorrow. Hurry now!' Martin was already peeling off his grey jumper as he followed his mother into the house.

The sun had risen high in the sky and was beating down on the lonely small figure of Roberto by the side of the road. It seemed much hotter here than out on the plains behind his village. Perhaps it was the effort of walking. He was tired, but excited too, by this great adventure.

But above all, he was very thirsty. Roberto sat down and took out his water bottle. Better have just a few mouthfuls. He had a long, long way to go. He ate a couple of the bread rolls, too, for he was hungry after walking all morning.

He looked up. High in the blue sky above he could see a great black bird slowly wheeling, waiting, scanning the ground. That was unusual: condors were normally to be found in even higher mountain areas. It was looking for some dead animal or a young llama or sickly sheep on which to swoop down. Roberto could hear bleating in the distance. He thought of David, and hoped the condor wouldn't worry him. They were huge birds, with a wing-span of nearly three metres. David was only a small boy.

Roberto lowered his gaze and his eyes rested on the clumps of spiky ichu grass around him. They were very sharp – he'd had to be careful where he sat. Apart from the dry scrub and one or two eucalyptus trees, there wasn't much else growing so high up, and especially at that time of year: winter and the dry season.

Apart from a couple of mud huts in the distance, and a group of alpacas and llamas grazing on the sparse, dry grass, there was nothing to be seen on the plains. So high up, yet so flat, the land stretched away endlessly into the distance, dry, so dry. Roberto could just see faint blue hills on the horizon. People had told stories of those hills and the big lake which lay behind them. There was supposed to be a huge hoard of gold at the bottom, somewhere. But no one had ever found it.

Roberto suddenly felt drowsy. The heat of the sun on top of a slightly less empty stomach made him want to lie flat out by the side of the road. He should be safe for a while, no one would even know he'd gone until sunset. He'd just have a little sleep . . .

He was wakened some hours later by a lorry flashing past him, leaving a trail of dust which nearly choked him. He wondered how David was getting on, and had another sudden feeling of anxiety, wondering if the sheep would trust David enough to go home with him. He got to his feet and looked around. All was just as before, except that the sun was sinking opposite the blue hills.

For the first time, Roberto began to wonder about where he would spend the night. He knew he might freeze to death if he just lay down by the road. The wind was already feeling cold, as the sun sank lower and lower – so quickly, it seemed. Roberto hurried on. He couldn't even see the town. How much further would it be?

He wondered what would happen to him if he did die of cold and exposure. Would the Great God look after him? But why should he be interested in a little shepherd boy? All the same, Roberto found himself saying in a frightened little voice, 'O God, please let me find somewhere safe tonight!' Then he began to run.

It could not have been more than two minutes later when he heard another lorry on the road behind him. Maybe that was the answer! People often travelled by lorry, didn't they? He turned round to face it and held up his hand. Would the driver see him? What would happen if he didn't? Not many vehicles used that road.

To Roberto's relief the lorry began to slow down. The driver stuck his head out of the window. 'Hola! Where are you heading for? I can take you as far as the town.'

Roberto scrambled in and sank thankfully onto the

blanketed seat by the driver. It was the only space left. In the truck of the lorry several other passengers were crowded onto sacks of potatoes.

'Where are you going?' The question was asked kindly, and as Roberto looked at the driver's face he hesitated only a moment before pouring out his story.

'But please, sir, is the town very big?' he asked fearfully. 'Do you know it well? I'm not sure exactly where my aunt lives.'

'Yes,' said the driver thoughtfully. 'I know the town very well. I teach in one of the big schools there. What's your cousin's name?'

Roberto told him, and looked at the man with awe. He was a school teacher!

'I know him. He's in one of my classes. He's taking part in the big march past tomorrow.'

Roberto was lost for words. He just kept looking, not daring to move, lest he should discover that this was all a dream.

'I've got to go near your cousin's house to return my father's lorry. He sent me out to one of the villages this afternoon, to collect some sacks of potatoes from one of his brothers' farms. If you like, I could drop you off at the house.'

Roberto grinned delightedly. 'Thank you! Yes, please!' he whispered. Then his face fell.

'But what will they say? Can they help me go to school? I want to learn so much!'

'Why don't you talk to Martin's mother and your own parents? I'm sure something could be arranged.'

Roberto sat wistfully thinking, watching the kilometres disappear under the lorry's swift wheels. But when they reached the town, his eyes were all agog! Never had he seen so many houses all together! And so many people! It was almost a relief to see some pigs wandering down the road looking for rubbish. Animals were something the boy *did* know about. They made him feel more at home.

The lorry pulled up outside a large concrete house in a wide, pot-holed street. A dog barked wildly from the roof opposite. There was a high wall by the side, with a partly open door leading into a yard.

'This is where Martin lives,' said his teacher. Roberto climbed down. Now that he was really here, he found his chest was pounding. He licked his dry lips and peered timidly through the crack in the doorway. School uniform white shirt, with grey trousers and jumper, were blowing gently on a washing line strung over the cobbles in the yard.

He hesitated. What would Aunt Amanda say? Supposing she was angry? The lorry still waited, its engine running noisily. Roberto plucked up courage and banged hard on the door. Seconds later he was gazing up into the astonished face of his aunt.

With a farewell wave of thanks to the friendly teacher, he hugged Amanda and went in. She was a short, plump woman with a cheerful face. Explanations waited until after they had all eaten a plateful of rice and vegetables, but then the questions began! They sat up late, talking: Roberto, Aunt Amanda and Martin. Roberto told them all about how and why he'd come, and how he wanted to go to school. But he didn't tell them about his prayer on the road. Martin told Roberto all about the march past next day.

'You must come and watch it!' Martin insisted. Roberto was only too willing. He'd never thought much about Independence Day before, up in the hills as he had been with his sheep. He had the strong feeling that he was at the beginning of something new. It was exciting. But where would it lead? What would happen?

'Aunt Amanda, I want to go to school!' he burst out. She nodded understandingly. 'We'll see,' was all she would say.

They were all woken by the noise of fire-crackers next morning, announcing the importance of the dawning day – Independence Day. Martin was up straight away, for he had to be ready for the march past. It was a good day. The red and white flag streamed out from every roof top, and as Roberto heard the music of the National Anthem, he felt proud of his country, glad to be Peruvian. On every street people were selling delicious things to eat: hot sizzling kebabs, deep-fat fried doughnuts, refreshing cool drinks. People were out in their hundreds, talking excitedly and watching all that happened. Roberto felt good when he saw his cousin marching smartly, just like the soldiers marched, straight legs up and down.

That evening, as they gathered at home again, Aunt Amanda looked at Roberto over the supper table.

'Roberto, if your parents agree, I'm quite willing to have you come to live here with us and go to school with Martin. You would be company for your cousin, and it would be helpful to have another hardworking boy around the house, especially now your uncle isn't with us.'

Uncle Jorge had died a few years back. Amanda earned enough to keep herself and her only son quite comfortably, by running a small shop in the front of the house and by knitting jumpers of alpaca wool with their varying shades of white, brown, grey and black. She sold them to the tourists who passed through on the train. The foreigners loved the different patterns and

16

pictures of llamas which she knitted into her jumpers.

Roberto gazed at her, open-mouthed with joy. Live with them? Go to school? 'Thank you!' he managed at last.

He was too excited to sleep much that night, although he wasn't sure what his parents would say. His aunt refilled his water bottle and gave him a fresh supply of flat barley bread rolls as he set off once again, early the next morning. The town was quiet, for it was still a holiday, and Roberto began the route his aunt had showed him that would take him back onto the road home. But after half an hour, as he emerged from the town onto the flat plain, he didn't recognise it! He must have taken a wrong turning! He was lost! There were the blue hills, but they looked much nearer now. Perhaps if he made for them, he might see his road. He walked on.

The burning noon-day sun shimmered on the surface of the lake. Half-submerged mud huts broke the monotony of the endless blue, as sky and lake met. On the shore, several new corrugated iron roofs caught the sun and dazzled Roberto's eyes. A few animals munched slowly at bedraggled, drowned crops which had been rescued by boat from where they had grown in the former village. Halfway up a small hillside, from a slightly larger building, came the sound of happy singing.

Tired and fearful, Roberto hesitated. Then he crept up to the door and looked in. A crowd of children about his age turned their heads to look at him. Who was he? He didn't live here!

A teenage girl led them all in one more song, then a woman got up to speak. Roberto thought she looked very kind. He squatted where he was, too tired to bother about the staring faces around him. The woman was a foreigner, but she was speaking his language, Spanish. She was talking about sheep! Roberto listened more intently.

The woman went on to explain that Jesus, God's Son, was the good Shepherd and was calling his sheep to him. She read from a book:

"He calls his own sheep by name and leads them out . . . his sheep follow him because they know his voice. But they will never follow a stranger. . ." Roberto thought of David. But he wasn't really a stranger. The woman went on reading. "I am the gate for the sheep . . . I have come that they may have life, and have it to the full."

A full life? Wasn't that what Roberto was searching for? But what did that mean? How could he get it?

The woman paused and looked around. Fifty-one pairs of brown eyes looked at her. 'If you want a new purpose for living, give your lives to Jesus. Let him be your Shepherd. He will show you how to live.'

Roberto's mind was busy. He thought back to his prayer on the road to find a safe place to sleep. God had answered, hadn't he? And now he had brought him to this place, to hear exactly what he had been looking for.

After the meeting, Roberto had a long talk with Diana, the English woman, in which he asked Jesus to be his Shepherd and his Leader. Diana was going to be driving back to the big town in three days' time. If he'd like to stay till then, and learn more of the Bible, she could take him home. It wouldn't be far out of her way.

At the end of those three days, Roberto knew that he still wanted to go to school to learn to read and write. But now his reason wasn't so much to earn lots of money, though he still thought that would be nice! But more than that, he wanted to read God's book for himself, and share it with other people, just like Diana and Juana were doing. But how could he ever learn to read? Could God help him do that? Could God make his parents agree?

He told Diana about his hopes and fears. 'Well, then,' she said, 'How about if we take Martin and his mother with us? We can easily pick them up from the town first instead of going straight to your village. Perhaps your Aunt Amanda could talk to your parents.'

And so it happened. By the end of the two-week holiday, Roberto was back in the big town for the start of term, the proud possessor of a school uniform! And Diana's husband, Derek, had promised to take some of the church members to Roberto's village, to share the Good News about Jesus with them.

As Roberto followed Martin into the school yard that first morning, he whispered a prayer of thanks to his Shepherd. 'Thank you, Jesus, for bringing me here. Help me to learn well and be useful to you.'

As he looked up, he recognized the smiling face of the teacher who had given him the lift. He ran joyfully to greet him.

The day the petrol ran out

The pea plants looked healthy enough, thought Sara,
as she busily weeded the patch of ground which
belonged to her father. It was difficult, for the field had
been dug near the top of the steep mountainside, but
Sara was used to hard work. She straightened her aching
back and looked around her.

The village lay below her, hugging the hillside. Set
in a maze of footpaths, the rich red-brown and brick
houses with their red-tiled or thatched roofs looked
attractive in the sunshine. Donkeys, cows, pigs and
sheep roamed everywhere, and a few people could be
seen leisurely pottering about their work. One was
leading some llamas, laden with vegetables to take to
market, others were working together checking if their
tools were ready for ploughing as soon as the rains
stopped, while the earth was still soft. Women were
grinding fresh herbs on special stones outside their
kitchens, or picking through the piles of rice to take
out any grit before cooking it.

Everyone was making the most of the morning's
sunshine. By lunchtime, the sky would be heavy with
clouds, ready for the afternoon's downpour of rain, the

daily pattern at this time of year. It was always the rainy season from January to March, up here in the mountains of Peru. This year the rain seemed to be even heavier than usual, and the hillsides were fresh and green. Yes, Sara decided, the crops were growing well, even if the weeds were keeping pace with them!

She was glad about that. It was one thing less for her parents to be concerned about. Sara knew her parents were worried about things although they rarely said anything. She didn't understand what things, only that over the last few months it felt as if there had been a dark cloud over their house. Sara was afraid that one day the cloud would break like the rain-clouds did, that something awful would happen which would change their lives. She shivered, despite the warmth of the sunshine. Slowly, she picked her way down the mountainside towards her home.

Turning a corner, she almost collided with her father, herding the family's pigs into a new enclosure. Sara was used to working with the pigs, and willingly gave her father a hand. They were very young still, and squealed as she gently pushed them in: mostly little pink and black ones, though one was a long-haired brown piglet, which was Sara's favourite.

As she and her father walked back towards their house they could see the main road, winding like a snake, far below them. A very steep, zigzagging stony track led up to their village from that road, but few vehicles used it. Almost everyone climbed up on foot. It took about fifteen minutes to reach the lowest houses. There was normally an excellent bus service from the bottom of their hill into the town twelve kilometres away, and Sara, like many others, made the journey each weekday, for she went to school in the town.

But the oldest villagers were content to stay on their mountainside. For them, the rest of the world was like a dream, cut off as they were from even such useful things as electricity.

'Sara,' began her father, and then stopped. Nothing was hurried here, not even conversations. Sara looked at his hands rough and gnarled with hard work, and then up into his kindly, crinkly, but anxious face.

'Yes, father?'

'There are rumours of landslides on the central highway.' Sara knew he meant the main road, as it wound round the mountains the other side of town, up to about 4,800 metres where lay the highest railway in the world, and then followed the river down towards Lima, the capital city, and the sea. It was a day's journey on the bus. But if there were landslides, no buses could get through, perhaps for weeks. Nor could anything else for that matter. Sara was glad her father was a good farmer, and they always had food stored up at home.

'My teacher spoke of it at school this week,' Sara answered. 'He told us that the rains had been heavy, and had washed mud and boulders into the river. It has risen so high and is flowing so fast that it has washed away the road in some places, and some houses, too.'

They fell silent, trying to imagine the horror of seeing your home swept away in the mud and water, with all your precious belongings.

'Truly, Sara,' said her father at last, in a low tone that she could barely hear, 'Our people have suffered much, and are still suffering.' He sighed, thinking of his own problems which he could not explain to his young daughter.

On the central highway, about an hour and a half's

drive up from the capital, a petrol lorry climbed steadily up the winding grit road. It was raining up here. On the left, the great river Rimac roared and swirled like a ferocious giant. Barely three months ago it had been a little trickle as it leisurely coursed its way down through the valley. Green fields had banked it in many places, where people tended their crops. But now the fields were under the river, and as Efrain, the lorry driver, watched the fury of the grey-brown water, swollen with mud and rocks, he turned to his companion.

'It's ugly, Adan! It's going to be no joke to get this petrol through. I don't like the look of it at all.'

'I know. They said in Lima that things were getting bad, but I didn't realise *how* bad,' replied Adan. Efrain drove on for a while, slowly because of the rain and the slippery mud on the road. Then he pointed ahead.

'Look! There's another lorry just ahead of us. At least we're not the only ones!' Even as they watched, a boulder in the hillside broke loose and came crashing down between them and the other lorry. It bounced onto the road together with a heap of loose earth and stones, and finally plunged into the swirling foam of the river. Efrain pulled up, and the two men got out.

'Grab the spades. There's not much to shift. Most of it's gone into the water,' said Adan. They set to work, clearing a path through. Then they gingerly started up the motor again.

'One more like that, and I'm turning back!' Efrain said grimly. 'It wouldn't have been funny if we'd been underneath that lot!'

It was just ten minutes later when they rounded a bend in the hillside, that they pulled up again, horrified at what lay ahead of them. The bridge, which normally they would have driven over, was now just a heap of twisted metal, and the other lorry was upside down in the river, being ripped and tossed about as if it were no heavier than a matchstick.

Horrified, Efrain turned the lorry round. That was no easy task on a narrow, slippery road. As they stopped for one last look, they heard a shout.

'Wait! Wait for me! Take me back with you!' It was the driver of the other lorry, who had jumped clear just in time as he realised what was going to happen. He had taken shelter further up the mountainside, and now came slithering down. He ran towards the petrol lorry. He was pale with fear, and his teeth were chattering. Adan opened the door.

'Hop in! My goodness, you had a near escape! Have a mug of hot chocolate to warm you up!' Adan reached behind for the flask they'd brought with them, and Efrain started driving the vehicle back towards the safety of the city, where even now, no rain had fallen, but where the torrential river was surging its way out into the sea.

Sara went off on the bus as usual next day. She enjoyed the feeling of being old enough to travel alone, though there were usually others from her village on the same bus. Today, for once, she didn't see anyone else she knew. Other parents had played safe and kept their children at home. But Mr and Mrs Perez were so wrapped up in their present problems that they hadn't even heard the rumoured warning about the town's public transport. The local radio station had stated that it was likely the buses would stop running by mid-morning, unless the expected petrol for them arrived. The garages were all running out, so the buses could not fill up.

School began at seven thirty and normally finished at half past one. Halfway through the long morning the news came through. The petrol lorry had had to turn back to Lima, so there would be no more buses until after the rains had stopped, and the bulldozers and engineers had been out to clear, repair and rebuild the central highway. At the mid-morning break, Sara talked to her friend Catia.

'I don't know what to do. However am I going to get home?' she asked.

'You could stay at my house,' offered Catia.

'But it might be weeks and weeks.' Sara was worried. Catia thought for a while. There were no telephones, no way of sending a message to her parents. Even if Sara were to stay with her, her parents would be worried.

'I've got an idea,' Catia said suddenly. 'Why don't you come home to lunch at my house, and then come with me to the Bible Club I go to? It's good fun, and maybe the leaders might be able to help. They're foreigners, but they speak our language and they're very kind.'

Sara considered this idea. 'I think that's about all I can do,' she answered. 'Thank you for suggesting it.'

Just then the whistle blew and they all trooped inside for lessons again. Sara found it hard to concentrate. How would everything work out?

As soon as school was finished, the two girls set out walking to Catia's home. They passed the market, where the women sat selling everything from potatoes to plastic buckets, in their layers of skirts, brightly woven shawls, and top hats over their long, black plaits. Small pigs ambled about in the streets, eating up the rubbish, and the sound of chickens squawking mingled with canned music and the noise of conversations. The 'taxi' tricycles wheeling people and their shopping home, and the harsh shapes of the hills around the town, looked familiar to the two girls as they wove their way through the streets.

It wasn't long before they arrived at Catia's house, and as they reached it the first raindrops began to fall. Quickly they hurried inside. Catia introduced Sara to her mother and explained the situation.

'You're welcome, Sara, make yourself at home!' said the motherly woman with a warm smile. Catia had seven brothers and sisters, and having Sara extra was no problem at all.

After their meal of pumpkin soup followed by rice and chicken pieces, Catia picked up her Bible and led Sara out into the street. Sara had never seen a Bible before, though she had heard about it. In her village they mostly worshipped in the small Catholic church and at the shrines in the rock faces. Sometimes they built piles of stones, or set up crosses on the roofs or the hilltops to ward off the evil spirits of the mountains. Sara remembered her grandfather telling the story of how he and several other men had thrown stones at a travelling preacher when they were young, because he was preaching from the Bible. Sara was curious to know what the Bible Club would be like.

They soon arrived at a house with steps up from the pavement to the front door. The man who answered the door led them into a large room with two patterned rugs placed neatly on the pink stone floor. Sara and Catia sank into an old sofa whose springs squeaked, and looked around them. On the walls were two shiny posters with beautiful pictures, but with words which neither Sara nor Catia could understand. However, there was also a carved wooden block and on it was written in Spanish, 'We love him because he first loved us.' Sara wondered what it meant. There were already three other children in the room, and more came in, until there was really quite a squash, with several children sitting on the floor. Then the man, whose name was Garth, came in with his wife, Melanie, and welcomed them all.

They began with some singing and games. Then the children divided into groups of two or three to go through some Bible Study questions prepared by Garth and Melanie. Sara was fascinated as she shared Catia's Bible and helped look for the answers. At the end of the study time all the children learnt a verse by heart. It was from Psalm 55:22, 'Leave your troubles with the Lord, and he will defend you.' Catia showed Sara where it was in her Bible.

For some reason she could not explain, Sara was excited by that verse. Yet she was puzzled, too. How could it be that God was interested in people's troubles? Surely, he was much too far away, and holy? If it really was true, then why did so many people still worry so much? She thought of her mother and father. Could it be that they didn't know about this verse? Well, she would tell them!

When all the children were sitting together again, Melanie read them part of a story. It was about some children who had found themselves in a land called Narnia. Sara listened, all ears. Just as they got to an exciting part, Melanie closed the book.

'We'll go on with the story next week,' she said, and the children sighed. 'Let's all stand, now, and we'll say a prayer before you go home.'

When all but Catia and Sara had gone, Catia

explained about Sara's difficulty to Melanie. 'So you see, Melanie, I thought you might be able to help,' she finished at last.

'Why don't the two of you come into the next room with us and have a cup of tea and a bun, and we'll talk about what we can do to get Sara home,' suggested Melanie. Garth had already gone out into the kitchen to put the kettle on.

Sara had another question to ask. 'Melanie, can you tell me more about that verse we learnt? I don't really understand it, but I want to be able to explain it to my parents. They're always worried.'

'Come on, I see we've lots to talk about,' replied Melanie with a smile, and she showed them into the dining room where Garth was busy putting out mugs and plates. A pile of buns sat on a big plate in the centre of the table.

As they ate their way through the pile, Garth reassured Sara. 'I've a little petrol left in my car, so I can run you home with no problem,' he said. Sara thanked him gratefully. Somehow the buns tasted even nicer after that!

Then they talked. It was quite late, though not yet dark, when Catia bid the others goodbye and set off once more for her home. Garth picked up his car keys and Melanie followed him outside with Sara. By that time, Sara had a great deal to think about. Garth and Melanie had explained how those who trusted Jesus were part of God's family, and God himself was their loving Father. So, if one of his children were to come to him with their worries, he would work all things out for good, even though sometimes that included difficult times. Because God loves his children, they need never be afraid.

They talked about Sara's village, too, and her family. Sara told them about her two older brothers who were doing their military service far away in the great capital city of Lima. She spoke of her father's farm, too, with the animals, potatoes and peas.

The car pulled out of the town and onto the main road. It was the central highway, and would eventually lead down into the jungle. The light was beginning to fade, and Garth put the car lights on.

'It won't be long now,' he said. 'We must remember to take torches with us for the way down, Melanie. We don't know the footpaths in the dark like Sara does.'

They were silent for the rest of the journey, each one wrapped in his own thoughts. Garth was praying that God would open up a way for them and their church to work in Sara's village as well, bringing God's Word to her people. Melanie was thinking about Sara's mother and father. They must be wondering what had happened to their young daughter. Sara was going over in her mind what she had learnt that afternoon.

Soon they reached the foot of the hill where Sara's village was. They left the car there, and the three of them began the steep climb up. It was still raining. The grit road was muddy and slippery, and shapes loomed up unexpectedly as the darkness grew. Once they rounded a bend and came face to face with a donkey, which, together with a sheep and a goat, was being urged on by a small boy. One or two kerosene lamps could be seen shining from the lower houses, casting long, eerie shadows. By the time they reached Sara's house, it was quite dark.

'Sara, Sara! How wonderful that you're home!' Mrs Perez hugged her daughter, while her husband shook hands with Garth and Melanie.

'Pleased to meet you,' they were saying, and Sara quickly introduced them.

'This is Garth and Melanie, father,' she said. 'They brought me home because the buses stopped running. There's no more petrol in town, and nothing can get through on the central highway. But Catia took me to their house for a Bible Club, and we had games and stories, and it's all going to be all right!' she finished with a rush.

'Will you come in?' invited Mr Perez, studying the English couple thoughtfully. 'We have only a humble home, but you are welcome.' He led the way into the guest room. The floor was of earth, though the walls were plastered inside, and the room was furnished with a wooden table and benches. An iron bedstead stood on its side against one wall, and opposite it hung a faded photograph of Mr and Mrs Perez on their wedding day. Garth and Melanie sat down on the benches around the table, on which flickered the flame of a kerosene lamp.

Mrs Perez had gone to the kitchen, and her husband ushered Sara in the same direction. As she went, her voice could be heard chattering on. 'Daddy, there's a verse in the Bible which says, "Leave your troubles with the Lord, and he will defend you", and Melanie says that . . .' The door shut behind them, and Garth and Melanie looked at each other.

'I think God is in this, Melanie, don't you?' said Garth.

'Yes,' his wife replied. 'I wonder what will happen now.'

They were left alone for about twenty minutes, and then Mr and Mrs Perez came back, bringing a tray of enamel mugs filled with a hot drink. Then they left again. It was thought rude to watch the guests having their drinks! The drink was made with a sprig of fresh herbs, covered with boiling water, and left to infuse with some sugar. Water boils at a lower temperature high in the mountains, so it was not too hot to drink at once. Melanie found the sprig of leaves tickled her nose as she got to the bottom of the mug!

Soon Mr and Mrs Perez returned, and the four grown-ups talked about the news of the landslides and the bridges which had been destroyed by the fury of the swollen river.

'Is it like that in your country during the rainy season?' they asked. Melanie explained that the weather in England was different. It rained all the year round there, and floods were rare.

'How is your family?' Garth turned the subject onto other things. Mr and Mrs Perez obviously trusted them, and out poured all their worries and problems. They talked and talked. Once Sara appeared in the doorway and said goodnight and thank you, but they talked on long after that. At last, Garth said they would have to be going.

'Will you stay the night?' Mrs Perez invited them.

'Thank you, but it's not far once we're on the road,' replied Garth.

'Well, let us escort you to the road. It's a dark path even with your torches, when there are no stars to help,' said Mr Perez.

'Thank you very much. That's very kind of you,' responded Melanie, thinking how brilliant the stars could be on a cloudless night here, so high up.

They set out together, Mr and Mrs Perez bringing a kerosene lamp with them which helped considerably. When they reached the car, they said goodbye.

'Thank you for your hospitality,' said Melanie

warmly.

'Thank you for bringing Sara, and for helping us understand about God's truth,' the couple replied. 'Now we are trusting him, we know he will help us in our problems, even when things are very difficult. Goodbye. See you when there's petrol again.'

Next morning, Sara was up early. She fed the pigs, and then climbed up the hillside to where the peas were growing. There were still plenty of weeds to pull up! She set to work with a will. Just before lunch she looked up and saw her father climbing the hill towards her. She ran down to meet him.

'Father, the peas are growing well! May I go to the Bible Club every week when the buses start running again?' Sara's face had a sparkle about it which her father hadn't seen for a long time.

'It's about that that I've come to see you, my dear,' replied her father. 'How would you like it if we had a Bible Club here, for the children in our own village?' he asked. Sara nodded enthusiastically. He went on, 'Garth and Melanie said they would be very willing to come, once they can travel about again. We've agreed to hold the Club in our house, and maybe one day we can have a meeting for mums and dads too, so we can *all* learn more about God.'

Sara noticed that instead of looking worried, her father's face was shining with excitement, as he continued, 'Meanwhile, they've lent me their Bible, and we're going to read some every day, when we've finished eating lunch, you and your mother and I.'

'Let's start today, father!' was Sara's glad reply.

As they sauntered down the mountainside towards their home, Sara looked again at the distant road curling among the hills far below them. It was empty of traffic, though she could just see a man leading a herd of llamas along it. In the opposite direction lay the town, and school, and Catia. But there too lived Garth and Melanie, and one day they would be travelling the road again, bringing God's message to her people. She squeezed her father's gnarled, brown hand, and they entered the house together.

The Inca trail

'Hallooooooooo. . .!' The occupants of the bus jumped with fright, and then burst out laughing. Admittedly, a few were laughing because they were nervous; the narrow road with its precipitous drops and steep, hairpin bends was enough to set their nerves jangling without that sudden cry as well. But most of the tourists to the ruins of the ancient Inca city laughed because it really was very funny. There was the young boy who had helped check their tickets at the top, and he'd raced them to this point! That was pretty good going, straight down the mountainside! He must be as agile as a mountain deer!

They continued their twenty minute zigzagging journey towards the bottom where the train waited which would take them back to Cuzco, and where the river could just be seen curling its way, as if practising, before becoming part of the great Amazon. Once or twice the bus had to pass another coming up. The passengers nearest the sheer drop only inches from the window closed their eyes tightly as the two vehicles squeezed past each other. Then as they rounded another bend, suddenly they all heard it again:

'Halloooooooo. . . !' There was the same boy once more!

By the time the passengers had reached the railway station at the bottom of the hill, along eight kilometres of winding road, the lad was waiting for them, having hallooed them at least four times. Holding out his woollen hat, he silently pleaded for a reward for his efforts, and was not disappointed. To be sure, most of the money would be given to his employer, but he was allowed to keep a little for himself. Grinning his thanks, the boy hopped onto a bus waiting to take yet more tourists up to the ruins, people who would in their turn be entertained in the same way on their return journey.

The boy's name was Luis, and he was ten years old. When he was seven, his parents had been tragically killed. He had lived rough for several months, eating what he could find in the semi-jungle area on the lower slopes of the Eastern Andes, near the village where he'd been born. Then one day he had met a man working for the tourist board about seventy kilometres further up the valley, at the ruins of Machu Picchu, the 'lost city' of the Incas. Eduardo had invited young Luis to work for him in exchange for a bed at night and one good meal a day. What Luis earned would go to Eduardo, except for ten per cent which he was allowed to keep, and with which he could buy bread for breakfast and supper. It meant constantly working, running down that mountainside, or else he would go hungry. But Luis didn't mind hard work. He always enjoyed watching the tourists' surprised and amused faces as he hallooed their bus. He enjoyed the thrill, too, and the surefootedness of one used to the mountains.

Luis loved the mountains. The ancient city had been built on an almost inaccessible hill top, over two thousand metres above sea level, surrounded by deep chasms and other high mountains beyond them. No wonder the Spaniards had never found it when they conquered the Inca Empire in the sixteenth century! Being so near the jungle, the hillsides were always lush and green, with tropical plants and vegetation. Luis was fascinated by the history of his ancestors. Soon after he began working at Machu Picchu, he had asked Eduardo about the ruins.

'No one really knows why the city was built,' Eduardo replied. 'It may have been a religious or military centre. It's still a mystery. Most of the remains that were found belong to women, the sun-worshippers, perhaps.'

'Tell me about the sun-worshippers, please, Eduardo,' asked Luis.

'Well,' was the reply, 'every important Inca town had a great carved stone, called an Intihuatana, or sun-clock, which marked the days on which the sun passed overhead at noon. At this moment, the upright in the centre of the stone cast no shadow.' They were standing by the sun-clock in Machu Picchu, and Luis looked at the great piece of white granite rock, smoothed on top except for the tall post carved out of the centre.

'It was a time for great celebration,' Eduardo continued. 'The High Priest of the sun god, Inti, poured out an offering of our special maize beer called chicha, while the people chanted a hymn to the sun, thanking him for his warmth and light, and for his son the Sapa Inca. Then they all drank and made merry.'

'The Sapa Inca was the Emperor, wasn't he?' Luis wanted to check on his facts.

'Yes, and he was the child of the sun. He ruled everyone for their good, just as the sun made the plants grow and the animals feel well.'

As Luis learnt more and more about the ancient Incas, he began increasingly to feel at home in his new surroundings. After all, he had Inca blood in his veins! Often, in his imagination, he would pretend he was living in Inca times. While he ran down the mountain-side, he would be a 'chasqui', one of the special runners who between them took messages many hundreds of kilometres from one part of the empire to another. He knew that the empire had once covered an area of over 3,000 kilometres in length.

When the tourists had gone and the sun was setting, he would wander through the empty, roofless rooms of the old city and be an 'amauta' or learned man, recording information on the 'quipus', the knotted strings which served instead of pen and paper. He would look at the amazing walls of fitted stone, assembled so carefully that a knife blade could not be forced between them, and imagine he was the stone mason in charge of building the city. He would make sure it was well built to withstand earthquakes!

When he came across a llama wandering on the green grass between the ruins, he would remember how the Incas had not discovered the wheel, so there were no lorries, not even carts. They used llamas to carry their goods from one place to another. So Luis in his imagin-ation would pretend he was in charge of a convoy of llamas, travelling up to twenty kilometres a day along the Sacred Valley of the Incas as far as Cuzco, over a hundred kilometres away.

Luis had never been to Cuzco, but he knew it had once been the capital of the Inca Empire. He longed that one day he might go there. He felt that if only he could, he might discover some great secret, perhaps something to do with the sun-worshippers? He didn't really know. He only felt it in his bones.

'Luis, you're day-dreaming again! Come on, there's another bus-load of tourists about to leave!' Eduardo was calling urgently.

'I'm coming!' Quickly Luis ran to help check the tickets of each passenger. Then he waved them off. Two minutes later, *he* was off, as agile as a mountain deer, taking the route he knew almost blindfolded, now, straight down the mountainside.

It was after the second 'halloooo' that it happened. Luis never discovered why, but he suddenly lost his footing, slipped, and fell. He rolled over and over, faster and faster for thirty metres, until he landed like a dropped stone on a section of roadway below. His last memories were of a terrible pain in his right leg, and then he lost consciousness.

Pedro and Nury Galván looked at their sleeping son and then at each other. Nury could see less anxiety in her husband's face now, and that helped her own to relax. Eleven year old Abner was out of danger, and was sleeping peacefully. There was no need now for both of them to watch him. Pedro rose quietly.

'I'll go back now, love, and get a few hours sleep. Then tomorrow night I'll watch him while *you* sleep,' he whispered.

'OK,' Nury replied in a low voice. 'It's silly for both of us to stay all night. If he wakes, I'll be here to give him anything he needs, and if I can't, I'll call the nurse.'

'Let's pray Nurse is not too far away if it's urgent!' was Pedro's final comment as he slipped out of the ward.

All the patients had to have someone with them each

night if possible. Nurses only came if it was really urgent; they had a lot of other patients to look after as well, and relatives could easily care for the non-urgent things.

Nury yawned, and clenched her fists in an attempt to fight off sleep. It had been such a shock when Abner complained of that sudden pain. They had taken him in a taxi to the hospital, where the boy was operated on immediately. That had been this morning. For a few hours he was very ill, and Pedro and Nury sat praying together. They were Christians, and belonged to a church in Cuzco. Abner was their only child, and Nury was not able to have another. What would they do if he died? They prayed that God would do what *he* wanted. They did not understand what God's purpose might be in allowing this to happen to their son, but they knew he would never allow anything to happen which he could not use for good.

In the early hours of the morning Nury looked up as she heard the sound of another trolley returning someone from the operating theatre. She wondered who it was. The person was quite small, possibly a child. She checked the machine called the drip that was allowing life-giving medicines to flow into Abner's veins. Yes, all looked quite normal. She closed her eyes for a while. Her head jerked forward and she woke with a start. It wouldn't do to drop off!

Her eyes roamed the ward again. There were four beds; the next one was still empty, and the one opposite contained an old man who had broken his toe. He was snoring gently. The other, in the opposite corner to Abner's, was that of the newcomer. He *was* a child, a boy. He looked about Abner's age. There was no one with him. He was having a blood transfusion – he must be in a bad way. Nury wondered what had happened.

Abner stirred, and instantly his mother was wide awake. But it was only for a moment. Nury relaxed again. It was five o'clock. It would soon be growing light. Already she could hear the early buses rumbling past the hospital on their way to the centre. All over Cuzco, people would be starting to prepare themselves for another day's work. She suddenly felt very weary. When Pedro returned just after seven, he found his son beginning to wake up, but his wife was fast asleep on her chair!

The first bus to come up from the railway station spotted Luis sprawled on the road, and quickly passed the message on. Eduardo and one of the girls working in the Tourist Hotel just outside the ruins, came down in an empty bus, took one look at the boy's leg, and felt sick. There was no question of an ambulance. For a start, there was no road for the first part of the journey between Machu Picchu station and Cuzco. The Sacred Valley of the Incas was a narrow gorge, just wide enough for the rapids-strewn river and the railway. Even the train had to go *through* the mountain in places. The next train was not due to leave until four-thirty. It was two-fifteen now.

Eduardo could see the break was a bad one. It was swelling a bit, too. That meant bleeding. It was urgent to get the boy to hospital as soon as possible.

'He looks bad, Lucy. One shouldn't move a person with a broken bone but how else can we get him to hospital?' said Eduardo.

Lucy looked on helplessly. 'Well, let's try not to move the leg more than necessary,' she answered. 'If you take his weight, I'll try to hold his leg still. We've got to get him down to the station somehow!'

They did their best to stop the leg from moving, and carefully lifted the boy into the empty bus. Very, very slowly they drove down. Luis was still unconscious. Half an hour after they reached the station, the train sidled in. It would still be an hour before it was due to leave. Eduardo spoke to the driver.

'Look, old man, we've a badly broken leg here. He needs to get to hospital in Cuzco urgently. Can we put him in the guard's van? It'll be too risky to lay him in a passenger carriage with all the comings and goings, and people wandering in selling food and so on. I'll pay his fare, of course,' added Eduardo.

'That's all right, mate,' responded the driver. 'We'll look after him. I'll leave bang on time. Can't leave any earlier, because this is the last train. Mustn't leave the tourists stranded!'

'I'll accompany him, of course,' said Eduardo. Gently they laid Luis on a blanket on the floor of the guard's van.

The girl left to return to her hotel duties, and Eduardo sat thinking. This was a bitter blow. He was fond of the boy in a way, and would be sorry if he could not work for him any more. But more than that, he worried about the hospital fees. He would obviously pay the immediate costs of an operation, for he would not leave Luis to die if he could prevent it, but after that . . . what? It would be months before the lad was able to walk again. Eduardo knew he could not afford to keep a boy who brought in no income, let alone pay for extended hospital treatment while he got well. He looked at him again, and then shrugged his shoulders. Maybe Luis would just have to join those who sat in crutches begging on the pavements.

At last the train began its five hour journey to Cuzco. It seemed a great deal longer than that to Eduardo, especially when Luis began to gain consciousness, and so became aware of his pain. He moaned; perhaps he had no energy to scream.

At the station in Cuzco, Eduardo quickly found a sympathetic taxi-driver, and within minutes the boy was in the Casualty department of the big, modern hospital. The staff made preparations, and Eduardo left a sum of money to cover the cost of everything in the first week. Even aspirin had to be bought!

Once Luis had been wheeled into the operating theatre, Eduardo went out to find a room in a hostel where he could spend the night. Tomorrow, he would call in at the hospital before getting the train back to Machu Picchu. Work was pressing; he could not stay longer. He had done his best.

Abner lay on his bed, watching all that was going on. A nurse came in with something for the old man. Poof! What a smell! Outside the ward there were quiet clankings, telling of normal hospital activities. Abner closed his eyes. He was still very drowsy. He felt much better today, as long as he didn't try to move. He could hear the nurse move on to the next bed, and attend to the person in it. Abner opened his eyes. She was wheeling away a tall pole thing with an empty bottle attached. He closed his eyes again and fell asleep.

When Abner next woke, he found his parents sitting on either side of his bed.

'Hallo,' he murmured.

'Oh, Abner, you're awake! Have you slept well? How are you feeling this afternoon?' Nury asked him anxiously.

'All right. Hurts if I move,' her son replied.

At that moment, a man was shown into the ward. He went over towards the corner bed and spoke quietly.

'Luis? Luis, it's me, Eduardo.'

There was a slight movement, and the boy opened his eyes. 'Where am I? What happened?' he cried softly.

'You fell and hurt your leg. You're in hospital in Cuzco. Don't try to move.'

'Cuzco?' The boy's head was swimming, but the name had a reviving effect on him. 'In Cuzco?' he repeated, 'Where the Incas were?'

'That's right, Luis,' said Eduardo, glad to see more colour in the boy's face. 'I must go now, back to Machu Picchu. They will look after you here in the hospital. You must be brave. Goodbye!'

'Goodbye,' replied Luis sleepily. His eyelids closed and he sank once more into sleep. Eduardo stood up and took a last look at the boy.

'May the spirits be kind to you!' he murmured, and quietly left the ward.

Pedro overhead enough of that conversation to realise the boy was unlikely to have any further visitors. He made a special point of going over to his bed on each visit to the ward, and speaking to him. Gradually Luis began to be able to sit up. He spoke very little, but answered Pedro's questions.

'Where do your parents live, Luis?'

'They're dead.'

'Where have you been living? Who looked after you?'

'In Machu Picchu. I earned my keep by helping with the tourists.'

'What did you do?'

The face of the boy became suddenly sad as he answered. 'I used to run down the mountain, racing the buses and surprising the people. They used to pay me . . . Pedro, will I ever get better?'

Pedro didn't know how to answer that. He talked things over with his wife that evening.

'Nury, can we do anything for the boy, Luis? The hospital say they've been paid enough to keep him in until he can get about on crutches. But then what? He has nowhere to go, now. Nowhere! Surely God wants us to help him. But how?'

'Pedro,' replied his wife, 'let's pray together first, and then I suggest we mention him in church tomorrow. Maybe God will give us the answer.' So Nury and Pedro quietly asked God to show them what to do to help.

The following morning they went to the church service as usual. Pedro told the congregation what he knew about Luis and asked them to pray for him. After the service, John, who was a foreigner helping with the work of the church, went up to Pedro.

'From time to time,' John told him, 'people in my country send me money to help people in special need. I have been wondering how I should use it. It seems to me that your Luis needs it right now!' He gave Pedro a wad of banknotes, smiled, and slipped away. Pedro stood gaping! That was a quick answer to one prayer, at least! Several other people came up, too, offering Pedro and Nury some money to help, and promising to keep on praying.

As a result, Luis was able to have the best possible treatment, and quickly responded to the love that Nury, Pedro and Abner showed him. When both the boys were nearly well enough to leave hospital, Pedro and Nury invited Luis to go home with them.

'That would be nice!' said Luis happily. For some

time he had realised he would have nowhere to go, and had been worried by it. But now, not only would he have a home, but he would be living in the old Inca capital!

The day came for them to leave hospital. Nury had given Luis some clothing Abner had grown out of, so he was well provided for. Pedro came into the ward, followed by a foreigner.

'This is John,' Pedro explained to Luis. 'He's going to take us home in his car.' Abner already knew him from church, and bounced up to greet him.

'Hallo, Abner, Hallo Luis! Nice to meet you,' John said warmly.

'Good morning!' Luis replied, always a little wary of strangers.

They left the hospital, Luis showing off how well he could use his crutches. He would need them for several weeks yet, but he was already learning how to get about quite expertly. All the same, as they crossed the courtyard and Luis had his first real view of the town, he began to feel sad again inside. He looked up at the hills that surrounded the city. How he longed to climb up and run down them!

Luis was put in the front seat of the car, because that was easier for his leg. John had never had such an excited passenger! Luis had never seen a place as big as Cuzco before. The houses had sloping red slate roofs, and many of them were built on Inca foundations, with the lowest part of the walls being the stones of centuries ago. The rest of the house was usually built in the style of the Spanish conquerors, with small balconies overhanging the narrow, cobbled streets.

They passed several ornate churches, and the cathedral in the main square, also built on the foundations of an ancient Inca palace. John showed Luis the street where there was a wall with a famous Inca stone which had twelve corners, all fitting perfectly. Many streets they passed were steep and winding, with steps up. They had been built for convoys of llamas, not for wheeled vehicles.

'The city is wonderful!' Luis blurted out, as they came towards his new home.

'You're interested in the old Inca stories, then?' asked John, parking the car carefully in front of the house.

'Oh, yes! Eduardo used to tell me so many wonderful things!' replied the boy.

'If you like, I'll take you all out to the fortress at Sacsahuayman, in a couple of weeks' time,' offered John.

'Oh, yes, please!' everyone said.

Slowly Luis was helped out; the family said goodbye to John and went indoors. It was the beginning of a completely different life for Luis. There were lots of things that were new to him. One thing was that every day, after breakfast, Pedro would take out a big book which he called a Bible, and read some of it, explaining what it meant. Then they would all pray together.

Luis found these times rather disturbing at first. He remembered how he had felt about Cuzco before he ever came, how he had sensed that here he might discover some great secret, perhaps something to do with the sun-worshippers. Well, clearly this family did not worship the sun, but they worshipped God, and his Son Jesus. There were many questions in Luis' mind.

Sometimes he talked to Abner, who was able to answer quite a few of his questions. Pedro and Nury could answer some of the others. He went with them to the church, and learnt many more things there.

Gradually he pieced together in his mind the story of how God had made the world, the granite mountains, the tropical plants, even the sun itself. He began to understand that God loved the world and wanted people to love him and obey him and live in a way that was pleasing to him. He knew that no one ever did so perfectly, but that God's Son Jesus had died on a Cross, which made everything all right somehow, for those who trusted him. He, Luis, trusted him! But how could he follow Jesus when he was tied to his crutches?

Two weeks later, John came back as he'd promised, and drove them all out to Sacsahuayman. Luis was thrilled as he hopped about among the ruins, which were almost as impressive as the ones at Machu Picchu. He even managed, with a little help, to climb up with his crutches and sit on the top.

'Hey, Luis, can't you just imagine the old Incas standing up here protecting Cuzco from attacks!' shouted Abner, racing over to join his friend.

'Yes!' replied Luis, who was already lost in imagination, and thinking too of Machu Picchu and Eduardo. Abner ran off again, and John came over to the boy. He sat down beside him, saying nothing, just enjoying the view and the peacefulness. After several minutes, Luis spoke.

'John, will I ever be able to run again? To be like I was before?'

John did not reply immediately. He prayed in his heart, and then said, 'Luis, the hospital said you would be able to walk again, but that you would never be as agile as you were before. I'm a Christian, and I know that sometimes God heals when doctors think it's impossible. But it may be, Luis, that God wants to teach you how to walk on a different kind of mountain.'

'What do you mean?'

For answer, John dug out his pocket Bible, and opened it at the last verse of Habakkuk. He read it out to Luis.

' "The Lord gives me strength. He makes me sure-footed as a deer and keeps me safe on the mountains." '

'Do you mean it was God who made me able to run down the mountainside at Machu Picchu?' asked Luis.

'He certainly did,' replied John. 'But it means much more than that. You see, Habakkuk is thinking about the difficult mountain paths of life. All of life is like a journey. If you're a Christian, you are walking on God's path where at the end is heaven. But often God's path is like some mountain paths, very steep and difficult. There are hard times and sorrows and pain, as well as joys and lovely times.'

Luis thought about this for a while. 'So, my crutches, and perhaps never again being able to run so well, are part of the mountain path of my life that God has chosen for me, and – what were those words again?'

'The Lord gives me strength. He makes me sure-footed as a deer and keeps me safe on the mountains.'

'So, God will help me to keep walking on his path.' Luis was beginning to understand.

'That's right,' continued John. 'And you are not walking alone on that path, for Jesus has promised never to leave us alone. He will be with you all the way, taking care of you.'

The sun was beginning to set, sending out rays which touched the huge granite rocks of the ruined fortress and turned them to gold.

So Jesus is the secret, thought Luis, not the sun-worshippers. One day, he wanted to return to Machu Picchu and tell Eduardo. But now it was time to go home. Pedro, Nury and Abner came to join them, and they all walked slowly over the grass to the car park. In Luis' thoughts was a prayer of thanks. If it wasn't for his accident, he might never have discovered Jesus, or known about God loving him. John turned the car, and they all headed for home.

God doesn't need binoculars

Hugging her snack box under one arm and a bag of books under the other, an English girl, tall for her age, emerged from the stream of grey-uniformed Peruvian children and made straight for the school gate.

'Chao! See you next term!' she called out to a group of friends just behind her.

'Happy Christmas, Jill!' they chorused in reply.

Squeezing between two parked cars containing waiting parents, Jill looked quickly around her, then crossed the road. A few metres further and she came to the main avenue. She waited to cross. Two grey-green buses, nose-to-tail, were ambling down the right hand side of the dual carriageway, and coming up the other side were three taxis, one private car, and a motor cycle. The latter overtook all the others in a cloud of dust, wobbling alarmingly it avoided a pot-hole, and disappeared with a roar round a corner. As Jill crossed she had to jump over an irrigation canal by the edge of the road, onto the pavement on the other side. Now she was in the small park.

A bee droned by her left ear as she skipped happily round the flower-beds and over the grass. It was the last day of term, and nothing could spoil her happiness. Not even the thought of next term. . . . Or could it? No, not today. Singing tunefully, she crossed the last road before running as fast as she could up the pavement to her home. Her older brother saw her coming.

'Hi, Jill! What are you so pleased about?'

'No more school for three whole months!'

'Hey, I thought you liked school!' Brian teased her.

'Well, yes, I suppose I do sometimes. But I like the holidays too, and tomorrow it's Christmas Eve! And I'm going to be in the play at church, and stay up till midnight, and . . .' Laughing good-naturedly, Brian took his sister's books and went inside with her.

Outside the house, the brilliant scarlet geraniums glowed in the hot summer sunshine. The patch of grass in the front garden looked a bit sorry for itself, since Mum and Dad, and even Maria, the girl who helped with the housework, had been extra busy with Christmas preparations and hadn't watered it for three or four days.

The houses around were neatly built and painted in pastel colours, but most of them had high walls, so it wasn't possible to see into their gardens. Some had iron railings instead of walls to make it more difficult for burglars to get in. Dogs wandered among the TV aerials on many of the flat roofs, or lay by the edge panting in the heat, tongue lolling, nose and paws just visible from the street below.

The sound of a gas van, first faintly, then gradually louder, reminded Jill Williams' mother that she needed a replacement gas cylinder. The horn parped constantly, and a man sat on the back edge of the open van, feet amongst the empty cylinders, banging their sides with a loud metal rod.

'Gas, señora! Gas!' he yelled for the umpteenth time that morning, as the van swung round the corner. Mrs Williams ran out and waved. The van squealed to a halt, and there was the sound of clanging as the man lifted out a new cylinder.

'How much is it now, please?' enquired Mrs Williams. The man growled a price as he hauled up the empty cylinder into the back of the van.

'Thanks a lot!' Mrs Williams gave him the exact money and called to her son as the gas van made a noisy departure. 'Brian, can you carry this in for me, please?'

'Sure,' said Brian, willing to show off his muscular strength. He lifted it up with one hand, thought better of it, and carried it in with two. He carefully put it down by the stove and wiggled it into position.

'Thanks, Brian. That should do us another month now,' said his mother, and continued chopping up the mangoes and bananas for fruit salad.

Meanwhile, Jill had changed out of her school uniform into shorts and T-shirt. 'May I go across and play with Susan after dinner?' she asked. Susan was Scottish, and her parents belonged to the same mission as the Williamses. She was a year younger than Jill, who was nine. Both of them went to the same school, and they had special English lessons taught by Susan's mother when the rest of their class learnt English. After all, they could speak it properly already! They could speak Spanish very well, too, after living in Peru for several years. Since all their other lessons were in Spanish, that was just as well! It hadn't been easy at first, though, and Jill in particular had hated her first term at the school, when she hardly understood a word. How different from this last year! She had loved her

Peruvian teacher. If only she could have stayed in her class next term. . . .

'I think Susan's mum is taking her into the town centre this afternoon for some last minute Christmas shopping,' said Mrs Williams in answer to Jill's question. 'And besides, if you want your costume finished for tomorrow night, you'd better be around for me to try it on you,' she continued.

Jill was to play the part of Mary in the nativity play put on by their church. In Peru, all the Christmas excitement is on Christmas Eve night. On Christmas Day itself, most people do nothing special at all, except the missionaries and other English-speaking foreigners. *They* always have a second Christmas celebration!

'Come and help me lay the table,' called her mother, and Jill ran quickly across the wooden parquet floor and into the kitchen. Ten minutes later, the family was seated at table, and Mrs Williams was dishing out pork chops and vegetables. Her husband thanked God for the food and they all tucked in ravenously.

Jill pushed her chair a bit nearer her father's. She was always glad when her father was at home, sharing dinner with them. So often he was away for a few days, for much of his work consisted in training church leaders in isolated villages up in the mountains, much too far away to return in a single day. He always took the car as far as he could, but sometimes he had to walk long distances after that, or even go by horseback where no car could travel. Jill and Brian loved to hear of Dad's adventures when he came home after a trip away.

His wife was always glad to have him home too, of course, but sometimes she was worried because he looked very tired and often came home with a headache. She was glad that now he would be home with them for three months. It was the start of the rainy season in the mountains, and usually the roads became so muddy it was almost impossible to drive on them. Mr Williams would wait now until they had dried out before going on any more trips.

After lunch was over, Jill went out to play in the garden while María washed up and then swept, washed and polished the parquet floor. Mrs Williams got on with sewing Jill's costume, Brian was absorbed in a crossword puzzle book his grandmother had sent him from England, and Mr Williams shut himself into his study to prepare a sermon for the following Sunday.

Jill sat very still in the tree house which Susan's dad had built them in the jacaranda tree, watching the garden below. A ginger cat came creeping down the path towards an unsuspecting sparrow on the grass. Jill tossed a twig to the ground and startled the bird, which flew up onto the wall just in time. The cat glared up at Jill and stalked off haughtily. A couple of blue dragonflies flew into sight just below her, and bees darted about amongst the geraniums in the flower bed. The hosepipe, in almost constant use throughout the year, lay coiled on the grass like an overgrown black snake. A long-tailed hummingbird hovered just a metre from Jill's face, its long, curved beak searching for nectar and insects in the mauve jacaranda flowers. The bougainvillaea hung like a purple curtain over the edge of the house.

Jill began to think again about school. Next term . . . but it would be nearly Easter when term began again. She had three whole months of glorious summer holidays before then! But next term would come eventually. It seemed to hang over her like a dark cloud. It was true she could forget about it very often, when there were exciting things to see or do, but every now and then it would creep up on her and overtake her before she realised it was coming. What would it all be like? A new class, with not just one new teacher, but several, this time. She remembered the comments she'd overheard in the playground.

'Oh, you don't have old Señora Condori for history! Poor you! She's a real dragon, isn't she?'

'It's having Señor Sandoval for games that's the worst. He's always telling me off. . . .'

Jill tried to remind herself that the two children she'd heard talking were actually very naughty and often needed telling off. But she still felt scared. What would it be like? She let herself imagine all sorts of horrible things that might happen. They went through her mind over and over again. Suddenly she let out a big sob and started crying. Her father heard her from his study which had a door into the garden, and came out quickly.

'Hey, Jilly, what's the matter, love?' he asked, helping her down to the ground, and wiping her tear-stained cheek with his hand. Jill only clung to him and sobbed all the more.

He knelt on the grass beside her. He waited a few moments. Then he spoke again. 'Did something happen at school? Has someone been unkind or spiteful to you?' he asked gently.

At the mention of school, Jill lifted her head. 'No,' she managed in between sobs. 'I'm frightened about next term.'

Mr Williams didn't say, 'Oh don't be silly', or, 'Well, forget it till after the holidays'. He took it quite seriously, and began to ask her some more questions. Gradually Jill calmed down a bit and was able to explain. After they had talked together for a while, Mr Williams said, 'I think it would be a good idea if we talked to Jesus about it, don't you? After all, he's going to be with you in the class next term, just like he's always with you, looking after you, isn't he? And I think he'd like you to tell him how you're feeling. You tell him, and I'll pray after you.'

So Jill closed her eyes and prayed. 'Lord Jesus, I'm scared about next term and all those new teachers who are so strict. Help me to know that you will be with me all the time.' Then her father added his prayer. Jill dried her eyes and went indoors with her dad. She felt a lot better, though she was still rather unsure.

She really was able to forget it in the excitement of Christmas Eve. That day, a special travelling market was in the Williams' part of town, and after lunch, Mrs Williams and Jill went out to buy some fruit and vegetables. Jill was glad of her sunhat. It was swelteringly hot as they picked their way through the stalls, looking for good, firm papaya fruit and sweet cucumbers, a round, yellow fruit with purple skin markings, which tasted a bit like melon.

Mrs Williams met someone from the Bible Study group she held weekly in her home. Of course, they stopped to talk, and Jill began to feel bored. Then she noticed the pumpkin lorry. It was a big vehicle, and the open back was full of enormous pumpkins. Some were nearly a metre across, and a man was sitting on one, chopping up another into slices for sale. Several women stood round the back of the lorry, waiting their turn to buy.

Just then, Mrs Williams said goodbye to her companion, and Jill tugged at her sleeve. 'Mum, can't you make some pumpkin soup? I do love it!'

'That's an idea,' replied her mother. 'I'd been wondering what to do for tea tonight.' The two of them strolled over to join the group of customers round the lorry.

After they'd returned home, and the pumpkin had been put in the pressure cooker, the whole family spent the afternoon wrapping up small gifts for a few friends, Susan's family and their own. Jill had thought very hard what to give Susan. In the end she had decided on two pink plastic bangles which she had seen one day on a street stall in the town centre.

After a late tea, it was time to leave for church. Mr Williams got out the car, and the family piled in. They didn't wear coats because it was still quite warm, though they had their jumpers with them. Jill was very careful not to crush the bag carrying her Mary costume. They passed through the area where the travelling market had been that afternoon. It was dark, and the headlights shone strongly onto the chalk lines which had marked out each stall-holder's area.

As they drove, they were aware of many more people than usual. They passed the end of the road in the town centre which led up to the main market, still open. The street was seething with people! Everyone was out buying at the last minute. Several times they passed buses, packed with people returning home, or going out to visit relations. Half a dozen youths would be leaning out into the road, holding on with perhaps one hand, feet only just fitting on the bottom step. Jill wondered if she'd ever see one fall off! The pavements were humming with excited chatter as the car rolled past, until they left the centre and continued down a long, straight, pot-holed road.

'We're nearly there!' Mr Williams commented, as at

last the car swung round another corner and a rough wall came into sight. They parked and got out. Mr Williams was careful to lock the car.

'Look, there's quite a lot of people here already,' said Brian, as he went through the corrugated iron gateway. The site had been recently bought, and the church members were meeting in a temporary building of loose bricks and corrugated iron roofing. The doors and windows were just empty spaces. It could be quite chilly after sunset, but now that summer was beginning it remained warm for longer in the evenings.

'Oooh!' Jill was surprised as she entered. The church had been decked out with special lights and painted backdrops for the dramas. Even someone's old curtains had been rigged out along a wire to cut off the 'stage'.

The nativity play was a great success. 'Joseph' didn't turn up, so Jill had to say all his parts as well as her own. The shepherds forgot when to come on, and had to be reminded in a loud voice which carried easily to the audience. But everyone enjoyed it and clapped enthusiastically.

After all the plays and poetry were over, and the church leader had spoken briefly about how Jesus, the Son of God, had come to earth as a baby at the first Christmas, it was time for presents. Each child in the Sunday School was given a small gift. For many, it would be the only one they received that Christmas, because poor families could not afford to give presents. After that it was time for a hot chocolate drink and paneton.

'What's paneton?' Jill asked Brian.

'Don't you remember from last year?' he replied. 'It's a sort of dry fruit cake with bits of green and red peel in it. It's traditionally eaten at Christmas here in Peru.'

'Oh, yes, I remember,' said Jill. 'Oh good, let's go and get some.'

They were halfway through eating it when they heard the cathedral bells chiming midnight. Instantly everyone put down what they were holding and they all greeted one another, the men shaking hands and patting shoulders, the women and children kissing right cheek to right cheek in the usual fashion.

'Happy Christmas! Happy Christmas!' they all cried. 'May God bless you!'

After a farewell prayer, everyone hurried home, the Peruvians to join with their families in their midnight Christmas dinner of cold chicken and vegetable salad, followed by more paneton and hot chocolate. The Williams, however, went home to bed. They would celebrate, English style, later on in the day!

It was two days later, when all the excitement was over, that Jill began again to feel that cloud of fear about next term. Was it really true that Jesus would be with her, even in Señora Condori's class? What about the games? Jill wasn't very good at games. Supposing Señor Sandoval was furious with her?

Mr and Mrs Williams noticed that Jill was quieter than usual. They prayed together that God would show her in some way that she could trust him for next term.

A few days into January, Mr Williams suggested a family outing. He was a keen bird watcher, and often on his trips into the mountains he would take his binoculars and stop the car to have a look at some unusual bird perched on a dry cactus or soaring over a valley. He was taking a week's holiday from the work he was doing, to spend time with the family.

'Shall I get a picnic ready?' asked Mrs Williams. 'I could easily boil some eggs and make a salad.'

'Yes, please let's go. I could look for beetles for my collection,' said Brian.

'And I want to find some wild flowers and press them to make birthday cards,' added Jill.

'You won't find many flowers!' commented Brian. His father broke in.

'I think she may, Brian. It's been raining a bit higher up. I think we all might be surprised at the difference.'

They set out in the car about an hour later, and took a road through one of the poorest areas of the city. Mr and Mrs Williams knew it well, for they often helped in the little church that had been formed there. They taught the members more about God, and were helping some of them to find work so they could support their families. The roads were all dry earth, and some of the houses were just crude blocks of stone one on another, with corrugated iron roofs held down by large stones. Some of the homes were more solidly made, but even in those there was no running water or sewerage, and they had only recently had electricity installed. There was rubbish all over the place, and, as always, stray dogs roamed all about. A few children, barefooted and dressed in scant rags, played in the dusty roads, noses running. One small child sat alone by herself, eating a banana with grubby hands.

Jill always found it difficult to understand. She thought of the children she'd known in England before they came. They all had so much! Jill was glad that her parents had come here to serve God where there were so many poor people. Maybe one day, when she was grown-up, God would call *her* to work here, too!

Soon they were out of the town, and winding up through deserty hillsides. A patch of yellow flowers caught Jill's eye, and at the same time her father shouted, 'Look, did you see it?' He, of course, was referring to a bird. They climbed for another half an hour until they came out into a slightly flatter part, where they found a spot to park the car. Mr Williams was quite right. It was much greener than usual. It was a cloudy day, bringing the promise of even more rain. The air smelt sweet and fresh. The four of them stood and gazed. Where a month ago it had been dry and barren, now all sorts of plants and grasses and small bushes were showing signs of life. Butterflies flitted from one patch of colour to another. It was still quite hilly, with footpaths clearly marked, but there were not the steep drops they had passed on the way up.

Mrs Williams unpacked the picnic basket, and they all ate hungrily. After they had eaten, Mrs Williams packed the things, gave a big yawn, and said, 'Well, I'm going to have a snooze and then read a bit. What are you all going to do?'

'I thought I'd climb up to that bit of rock above the bend in the road, and see what sort of view there is. I'll take my binoculars,' replied her husband.

Brian decided to stay nearby and search for his beetles, and produced a jam jar with lid.

'I'm going to wander down there and see what flowers I can find,' said Jill. She skipped off happily. It was Granny's birthday next month, and she wanted to press some really special flowers. Sometimes there were unusual flowers with very thick petals to retain water, but they didn't press very well. Perhaps the simpler ones would be better.

After about an hour, the sun began peeping out again from behind the clouds, and Jill began to feel dozy. Perhaps she would take back what she had collected to the shade of the car and join her mother for a rest. She looked up. Where was the car? She could see the road above her, curving round the hillside very gently. But there was no car. She looked around her, hoping to see Brian or her parents walking about or sitting on a rug. But there was no movement anywhere. Everything was silent. Not even a bird sang. The great volcano in the distance stared back at her from its vast height. The mountains seemed to go on for ever and ever. Not even a butterfly came into sight. She was alone. Completely alone.

A whirl of emotions passed through her. Doubt: had they forgotten her and gone home without her? Surely not! Fear: had something terrible happened like an earthquake, and they'd all disappeared? But she hadn't even felt a tremor, and certainly the volcano hadn't erupted! Panic: what should she do? Would she ever see her family again? She remembered stories of bears in the mountains and was about to scream in terror, when she remembered something else. It was the conversation she'd had with her father under the tree house in the garden. 'Jesus will be with you in the class next term, just like he's always with you, looking after you. . . .'

'Lord Jesus, please look after me now,' she cried out loud.

Meanwhile, Mr Williams had had an extremely interesting afternoon. Apart from several common birds, he'd identified two he hadn't seen before, and had made pencil notes, ready to look them up in his big book on South American bird life that he kept at home in his study. Now he trained his binoculars on his family. His wife was reading her favourite women's magazine sent regularly from England by a friend of hers. Brian appeared absorbed in something on the ground just a few metres away from her. Jill? Where was she? He focused his binoculars again. Ah, there she was, below the bend in the road, round the other side of it, with a bunch of flowers in her hand. She was staring into the distance with her back to him. Mr Williams thought he'd better fetch her. It wouldn't do for her to get too far from them.

He scrambled down the bank and walked along the road. He didn't run, for so high up in the mountains it was not wise to be too energetic until you were used to it. It could have an unpleasant effect on your body. When he reached a point level with his daughter he called her.

'Jill, Jill, let's go and see if Mum's packed any cake to have with a cup of tea, shall we?'

'Dad!!' Jill's glad shriek surprised him. It sounded as if she hadn't seen him for years! When she reached him, she hugged him as if she never wanted to let go.

'Hey, Jilly, have you been unhappy again? Are you still thinking about school?' asked Mr Williams.

Jill explained how she thought she was lost, and how glad she'd been to see him. 'But do you know, Daddy, I asked Jesus to look after me, and he was there all the time, wasn't he?'

'That's right, my love,' said her father, holding her hand as they walked back together. 'And God doesn't need binoculars to see you like I did!'

'You know,' confided Jill after a few minutes, 'that's helped me to understand. Now I know it's going to be all right next term. Jesus will look after me at school, just like he did here.'

'So you don't mind any more?' asked her father, inwardly thanking God for answering his prayer.

'No, I think I'm even looking forward to it,' replied Jill, 'It will be a sort of adventure. Jesus and me braving it together. Don't you think so?'

'I do indeed,' agreed her father.

Marcos and the proud chicken

The sun had already peeped out from behind the great volcano when Marcos ran down the steps into the yard, grabbed the tin of chicken feed and threw its contents into the coop. There was a flurry of feathers and a great deal of raucous noise, then one of the chickens began to feed triumphantly, squawking constantly at the others if they came too near.

Marcos watched with interest. Everyone else in the family thought this chicken was a nuisance, because it was difficult to tell if the others were getting enough to eat. It was always the same struggle for power in the coop, and always the same chicken won. But Marcos thought differently. He looked the chicken over. It was certainly doing well on it, getting nicely plump and healthy looking! He watched it retreat slightly, having had its fill, and laughed at the others nervously edging their way to what was left.

Marcos admired that fowl, for he had a streak in him which wasn't all that different. He thought back to a recent success.

It had been a cloudy summer's day a week ago, when little could be seen of the mountains which towered above the city, because of the mist and low cloud. There had been a football match between some of the local boys. Although at nine, Marcos was rather younger than the others in the team, he was picked because he was a fast runner and a good tackler. On hearing the news he spread it all round his classmates at school, and some of them turned up to watch the game. Being a slightly cooler day, Marcos' energy was even better than usual. But it was a pity that he had not yet learnt what teamwork was all about. As they kicked and dodged over the dusty, dry earth of the pitch – there wasn't a blade of grass in sight – Marcos made sure that most of the goal shots came off *his* boot. Never mind the rest of the team. His side won! He remembered how his classmates had slapped him on the back afterwards. What a brilliant player he was, to be sure!

'It was a good match,' he told his favourite chicken as his thoughts returned to the present. 'And you're a handsome creature. None of the others is quite so good-looking as you!' The chicken appeared not to notice either remark, but continued to preen its feathers.

Marcos looked round the yard. On the left was the kitchen/dining room, rather grimy with age now. He could hear his mother moving about inside, laying a plastic cloth over the worn table, and setting out the enamel bowls and mugs with a clatter. They did not need plates as the bread rolls would be eaten dry, straight from the table. An army of flies was investigating the area, attracted by the chicken coop nearby.

On the opposite side of the yard was the 'garden'. This was a walled-in bed of soil, watered by a hose, in which grew a number of prickly pears on a cactus, a fig tree, several different herbs and a long trailing marrow plant. A small dove was perched on the cactus, cooing its heart out. Across the yard was strung a series of wires, on which the family's clothes, washed by hand in cold water, would drip dry in a very short time, thanks to the dry climate. The ground beneath Marcos' feet was rather uneven concrete, cobbled in places, and leading down to some stone outhouses at the bottom. All the junk was kept there. Opposite them, leading up to the rest of the house, were the steps which Marcos had run down that morning.

Marcos continued to daydream. He'd done well at school last term! He'd managed to get high marks for every subject in the exams! He conveniently forgot that this was largely due to cheating. Even if he had remembered, he would probably have congratulated himself on being able to get away with it. In his mind, to be a good cheat and not get found out was almost as good, if not better, than obtaining a high mark. But of course, he was clever too, he reasoned.

He remembered overhearing a conversation in the playground one day. 'Have you remembered we've got a history test on the heroes of the War of the Pacific?' a rather fat boy was asking his much thinner companion. 'Yes, and I don't know anything, do you? I bet Marcos gets the top mark. . . .' Their voices had trailed off, leaving the subject of the conversation even more proud of himself than usual.

Then there was the church music band. Some young people had formed a group playing guitars, zampoña (pan-pipes), charango (a small, stringed instrument which used an armadillo shell for its base) and other Peruvian instruments. A friend of Marcos' older brother was the zampoña player, and when the group needed a drummer Marcos was invited to play. He had an excellent sense of rhythm, and actually tried hard to do what he was asked, but on the first performance in a neighbouring church's young people's meeting, Marcos had let his confidence and enthusiasm run away with him. He'd banged the drum harder than ever before, drowning the sound of the other instruments. He'd not been invited to play again, though he wasn't quite sure why!

He turned again towards his chicken. It was looking at him with its beady eye, in a way that made him feel slightly uneasy.

'Come and have your breakfast!' His mother's voice interrupted Marcos' thoughts, and he slipped into the room next door. The smell of burning met him.

'What's it this morning, Mum?' he asked. His mother, a tired, frail-looking woman, replied, 'It's cinnamon porridge. And bread of course.'

'Humph! I suppose that's all right. Can't I have milk?'

'You've plenty of milk in your porridge, though it boiled over a bit. Come on, I don't want any nonsense this morning.' She pushed a bowl at Marcos, and he ate in silence.

Nicolas pondered, and chewed the top of his ball-point pen. As he sat in the little room at the back of his house he could hear a group of sparrows arguing on the ground under the olive tree outside. A big, black bee made as though to fly in at the window, then changed its mind at the last minute. Nicolas considered the bee. It was said that its body was so heavy that it had to wait till after the sun had risen so that the warm air-currents could help it lift off the ground. Well, *he* needed some help to get his thoughts off the ground! He'd been sitting here for half an hour, and still didn't know what he would talk about. He prayed that God would show him what to say.

The church which Nicolas attended was planning a picnic. It would be for anyone with enough energy to walk over tough ground for an hour or two first. Most of the people were keen to go. There would be games too, and then a talk from the Bible. Nicolas, as one of the leading men in the church, had the job of giving that talk. He had his Bible on his knee, and pen and paper to hand, but so far, no thoughts. Today was Sunday, and they would be having the picnic on Friday, as it was a national holiday.

The sparrows were still arguing away, and Nicolas got up to see what it was all about. As he watched, a cat appeared from nowhere and a second later the argument finished abruptly, as all but one of the sparrows flew off indignantly to a nearby olive branch. *Now* Nicolas knew what he would speak about! He rustled the pages of his well-used Bible and read. Then he began to write.

Later that morning, Nicolas and Marcos met in the large, well-constructed church building. It was time for the weekly all-age Sunday School.

'Hallo, Marcos. Nice to see you! How are you?'

'I'm very well. Did you hear about the football match last week on the pitch round the corner?'

'Yes.' Nicolas looked thoughtfully at the boy. 'So that's why you didn't come to church, of course?'

'I won. I mean, my team won. Oh, there's my friend Raul. Excuse me, please.' Marcos hurried off quickly, leaving the young man wondering about him.

'Please will you all come inside now?' came the ringing voice of the superintendent. 'We're going to start.'

Marcos and Raul followed the others into the church,

and took a seat on a wooden bench on the right hand side, with the other children. Marcos looked around the church. He didn't come very often. His parents were Roman Catholics, though they didn't go to their church frequently, either. Marcos preferred to come here because it was nearby, and several of the local children whom he knew came along.

The building was far bigger than the congregation, but it was used as a kindergarten during the week, so all the space was necessary. The walls were painted pale green, though the right hand wall had obviously suffered from roof leaks on the few occasions when it had rained. A few damp-looking posters and charts hung bravely on that wall. The concrete floor was painted red, and was constantly covered in dust, as however often it was swept it was impossible to stay dust-free for long when it was so dry outside. A portable wooden pulpit stood on a platform in front of them, and a small, old kitchen table, covered with a cream-coloured, hand-embroidered cloth stood on the floor below it. On the table were letters, green plastic vases, a few drawing-pins, bits of chalk and old chorus sheets.

'We're going to start with the chorus, "Our God is so great",' said the teacher, and she began singing. Children, young people and adults joined in wholeheartedly. Even Marcos, who knew he had a good voice.

They were running late as usual, but nobody minded and gradually more people came into the church. After several choruses and a prayer there came a quiz.

'What was last week's memory verse? What was last week's lesson about?' The questions rolled on. Marcos, for once, was unable to answer a single one, because he hadn't been there last week. He'd been away at the football match. He dared not attempt what might turn out to be wrong.

After the quiz there was a Bible reading, and then everyone divided up into classes for the lesson. The adults stayed in the church, but Marcos' group took benches into one of the tin-roofed out-buildings next to the church.

It was when they were all back together in the church for the end of Sunday School, that Marcos first heard about the outing. He'd missed last week's announcement, due to the football match. He instantly decided to go. He whispered to Raul, next to him.

'Are you going on the picnic?'

'Yes, are you?'

'Yes. I haven't asked Mum and Dad yet, but I'm sure they won't mind. What do we do about food?'

'Oh, some of the women are cooking rice and eggs, and there's bound to be lots over. You might get asked to help carry the big saucepan, though.'

'Not if I can help it,' replied Marcos cheekily.

At that point there was a loud 'Ssshh' from the leader, and the boys looked up to find several eyes on them. Evidently they were about to pray.

When Sunday School was over, Marcos hurried home. His mother was leaning over the kerosene stove, trying to pump up the flame.

'Oh, Marcos, could you give me a hand with this? It doesn't seem to want to work this morning.' His mother straightened her back wearily.

Marcos liked any opportunity to show off his strength, and at once took over. Very soon there was a steady flame going and his mother thankfully put the soup on to warm up. Marcos thought this a good opportunity to mention the picnic.

'Mum, do you mind if I go out on Friday? The church is having a picnic. Raul is going. Can I?'

'Friday?' responded his mother, 'Yes, I can't see why not. Should keep you out of mischief.'

'Good. You won't want to come, will you?'

'No, dear, thank you. I shall enjoy a quiet day at home,' said his mother, and she stirred the soup again. Marcos dashed out into the yard and made straight for the chicken coop.

'. . . And my team will win the volleyball. You see if they don't,' he cried out to the chicken, which was looking plumper and prouder than ever.

The day of the national holiday dawned fine, with only a few white clouds in a blue sky. Soon the summer would be gone, and the skies would be more or less clear blue like that for the rest of the year. It was already the beginning of April, and although Marcos had been back at school for a fortnight, some schools had yet to begin the new school year. When they did, next week, it would be a sure sign that winter was on the way.

By about three quarters of an hour after the agreed meeting time, everyone was ready and waiting outside the church. A man called Juan was in charge, and he led the party up the dusty road through one or two streets, and then up a steep hill. At this point they had an interesting view. To the right there was bare desert reaching to the foot of the smoking volcano twenty kilometres away. To their left and far ahead stretched a large part of the city. Marcos could just make out the cathedral towers in the main square in the centre.

More immediately ahead was more desert, with lots of steep, dry valleys or ravines to cross before they reached a line of irrigated fields, and beyond them, the river. It was the river, with its grassy banks and areas where they could play, that they were all making for.

The group began the first descent of one of those dry valleys. The women and the older men took it carefully, feeling each foothold. With no branches or even tufts of grass to hold onto, it wasn't very easy, but they made it, and scrambled up the other side more easily, though breathlessly. The younger men took great strides, kicking away rusty tins, broken bottles and other rubbish. The children ran down amidst a great cloud of dust.

As they walked, the sun beat down on the barren ground, and the tiny fragments of stone in the earth caught the heat and magnified it. By the time they arrived at the edge of the fields they were thirsty and very hot. One or two had a bit of a headache. But now the going was much easier, and the feel of the green cabbages and beans on their ankles made for a cooler, more refreshing walk.

They carefully skirted the edges of the fields, slid down the occasional small terraced slope, and finally came to the river. How grey it looked! It smelt rather unpleasant, too, but they soon got used to that.

Led by Juan, the group crossed over by a little foot-bridge and turned off to the right. They slowly wound their way along a path until it widened into quite a large grassy area. Here the adults thankfully sat down; some of the children did too, but most of the boys were full of inexhaustible energy and continued to explore the river path. But not for long. Juan clapped his hands and announced that they would say grace for lunch. That brought the boys running back!

'I'm hungry!' 'Ooh, what a delicious smell!' Every-body chattered at once.

As the big white cloths covering the saucepans were untied and the lids were taken off, people began to form untidy queues. Marcos tried to push in, but was firmly put at the end of the line! He began to wail. 'What if it runs out before I get there? I'm starving hungry!' He was ignored.

However, there was plenty and to spare of the meal. There was soup, as always in a Peruvian dinner, picnic or no picnic. Then came rice and eggs with fried potato. It was almost cold by now, but that didn't matter! For the next twenty minutes, everyone was busy eating. A cold drink made from the juice of boiled up purple maize, with sugar and fresh lemon juice, quenched their thirst.

'Can I have some more? I'm still thirsty.' Marcos was holding up an empty plastic mug to one of the women church members.

'Sorry, there's none left now,' the woman replied.

'Why didn't you bring more?'

'Well, it's a bit heavy to carry all that way,' the woman began patiently. Then a man's voice interrupted.

'Here you are, Marcos. Have the last bit of mine.' It was Nicolas. Grateful for once, Marcos took the mug and drained it to the dregs.

'Thanks, Nicolas.' Then he sprinted off to find Raul.

Meanwhile, three of the young people fixed the volley net up between two conveniently placed low trees. Six people of all ages took their positions on one side and another six on the other.

'Can't I play?' came a familiar voice. 'I'm much better than Belia.' Belia blushed and looked as if she was ready to cry. One of the men on the team came to the rescue.

'Next game, Marcos. Belia's playing this time.'

Volleyball is a favourite game with Peruvians, and they are very good at it. They punched the ball to each other across the net, each team working hard to keep it from touching the ground. When eventually one of the teams won (and it was Belia's team!) Marcos was allowed to play.

Marcos tried to hit the ball every time it came over the net, often getting in the way of the other members of the team, and causing them to lose points. When his team lost, Marcos flounced off in a sulk, for once having nothing to say.

As no one seemed to be taking any notice of him, Marcos decided to go for a walk by himself. The happy shouts, and the smack of the ball being hit from side to side of the net, grew fainter and fainter. Marcos didn't really notice where he was walking, he was so wrapped up in himself. He was unaware of the birds singing in the bushes, and the drone of insects flying around him. He didn't see the tiny wild flowers half hidden along the edges of the river bed. Even the soothing scent of alfalfa growing nearby escaped him.

After walking for about twenty minutes, Marcos came to a point where the path had left the river bank to leave room for another field of cabbages. Below the field, on the bank of the river, was another grassy area, smaller than where the picnic was, but which looked inviting. The river looked more interesting there, too. Marcos decided to investigate. He was rather tired now, too, though he wouldn't have admitted it!

He carefully made his way down the edge of the cabbages and reached the river again. He sat on the bank, legs swinging over the water, and looked at it. It was quite shallow. Little eddies were forming around half-submerged rocks, making white bubbles which ran away into the current and disappeared. Marcos could see where parts of the river seemed to flow faster than others. Sometimes the surface was like glass, but in other places it looked more like chopped up jelly. There were stones and rocks of all shapes and sizes in the river bed, and to his left were some bigger boulders – some about a metre high – leading out into the river from a kind of pebbly beach area.

He scrambled to his feet. He liked the look of those boulders. And after all, he was very good at climbing things. He let himself over the edge, feet first, onto the 'beach', balanced, and then began to climb the first few boulders. One was wobbly, and he sprang off it only just in time not to fall into the water. One or two bits were quite slippery where continual sprays of water had encouraged algae to grow. But mainly they were smooth rocks, warm to the touch in the sunshine.

Marcos was enjoying himself. He was aiming for the furthest rock which was leaning over the water at a rather odd angle. He had almost got there, and was already feeling pleased with himself, when his left foot slid on a hidden bit of algae and he slithered off, slowly at first and then with a crash. His head hit another rock lower down and he lay unconscious, his face just a few centimetres from the surface of the river.

Meanwhile, the rest of the group had enjoyed their afternoon of games and the opportunity to sit by the river, chatting to each other. It was Nicolas who first realised that Marcos was missing. He was due to give his little talk in about an hour, before everyone returned home. But there was time to go and look for the boy first. Someone would have to, anyway, and better sooner than later. He had a quick word with Juan, who volunteered to go with him, and grabbed a warm jumper. It might just be useful!

Unless Marcos had returned home, there was only one path he could have taken, and the two men set out along it at a brisk walk, eyes skinned in all directions, ears alert for any unusual sound. As he went, Nicolas prayed that God would keep the boy safe.

They had walked quite a way before Juan suddenly stopped, shaded his eyes and said, 'Listen!' Nicolas stood still and listened. They could hear the flow of the water, increasing now. It must have been raining further up, and the water level was rising. One or two birds were singing their goodnight songs before going to bed. A dog barked from far off, and a cow mooed. And then – they both heard it this time – an unmistakable cry, 'Help!'

'It's coming from over there,' Juan said, pointing further ahead and to the right of them, where the river turned a slight bend. They could see fallen boulders jutting out into the water.

'He must have been mucking about on those rocks, the fool,' returned Nicolas. 'Oh, Marcos!' Quickly they ran ahead, looking for a way down to the river.

When Marcos came to, he was first aware that his head hurt dreadfully. Then, that he was very cold and wet, and thirdly that water was just tickling his chin. As he realised where he was, he tried to crawl out of the water, and found he couldn't! His left ankle was completely stuck under a small rock. A wave of water sploshed right over his face. This woke him up completely, and he realised that if he stayed there much longer he would probably drown! In panic, he managed to heave his chest up a little and onto a nearby rock. This was uncomfortable, but at least his face was out of the water.

He didn't know what to do! Maybe someone would come and rescue him? Then he thought of how he'd behaved, and realised they were probably glad he wasn't there, and wouldn't bother coming to look for him. For the first time in his life, Marcos began to see himself as he really was. It was so awful, and he was so uncomfortable, that he burst into tears.

He lay there sobbing for perhaps an hour, and then began to feel calmer. Perhaps it was that he had no more energy left. He had almost been lulled into an exhausted sleep by the monotonous washing sound of the water, when another wave splashed his face, and he realised the water was still rising. That was when he had first lifted his head and shouted for help. He couldn't hold it up for long, so he held his breath and rested it again on the rock. Then he raised himself to cry out again.

He'd almost given up after about twenty minutes of doing this, when he suddenly became aware that he was no longer alone. He felt a gentle pair of hands on his shoulders, while another pair was freeing his ankle from the rock. Best of all, a familiar voice was calling him by name.

'Marcos, it's me, Nicolas. Don't worry, we'll soon get you out of this. Just relax. Don't try to get up. We'll lift you.'

Sobbing again with relief, Marcos found himself being lifted onto the river bank. There he sat, dripping wet and shivering, and then he turned to Juan and Nicolas, sitting one on each side of him. They looked pretty wet, too, he noticed!

'Thank you! I'm sorry!' Nicolas wondered if perhaps that was the first time in his life that Marcos had used that word 'sorry', and was thankful inside.

'I think we need first to take most of your clothes off, Marcos. They'll soon dry off in this sun, and look, we've brought you a jumper to warm you up,' Juan said encouragingly.

That done, Nicolas prayed: 'Thank you, Lord, that Marcos is safe, and that you showed us where he was. Help him to learn something good from this. Amen.' They sat together for a few minutes more and then Juan spoke.

'I'll pop back and borrow one of those cloths the women used to wrap the saucepans. That should be big enough to wrap round you while your trousers dry.'

'Good idea, Juan. I'll stay here till you get back,' said Nicolas.

Juan sprinted back to base, and within minutes he had returned with a large white cloth. When Marcos was ready, they helped him to his feet and wrapped it round him. His left ankle still hurt a bit, but he could stand on it and there seemed no permanent damage. Slowly they helped him back to the picnic group.

The volley net had been taken down, and everyone looked ready to go home. Quietly Nicolas explained what had happened. Then he said, 'I'm going to tell you a story. . . .' He told them all about the cat and the quarrelling sparrows in his garden the Sunday before, and of how they had reminded him of a story in the Bible.

'Joseph was rather stuck-up when he was a young man. Because he was his father's favourite son, he seemed to think he was the most important person around, and didn't care a toffee for other people. So God had to teach him the hard way. He was sold as a slave, and got sent to prison for something he hadn't done. . . .'

Marcos listened intently. 'God had to teach him the hard way.' For the first time in his life, he realised that the Bible had something to say to him.

'You see,' went on Nicolas, 'God says in his Word that he resists the proud, but shows favour to the humble. He also says we mustn't think of ourselves too much, but consider others better than ourselves. . . .'

Marcos didn't hear the rest of the talk. Those words went round and round in his head. He thought of his chicken, too, but he was beginning to realise that it wasn't so clever after all.

He was a very subdued Marcos as slowly the group wended its way home that evening. Nicolas brought him to the door and gave his mother a quick summary of what had happened, reassuring her that he was perfectly all right except he'd probably develop a cold. As if to underline the point, Marcos sneezed!

There was a lovely smell of cooking as Marcos entered the yard. His mother looked at him anxiously. For once, he didn't go straight to the coop. He sat down at his place at table, and his mother said nervously, 'Marcos, love, we needed some chicken, and your father thought it was about time that proud, greedy one let the others fatten up a bit. So we're having it for tea tonight.'

She expected Marcos to shout and storm and rage. But instead, he quietly began to laugh. She looked at him, wondering if he'd understood what she was telling him.

'Mum, that's all right. You know, that helps me feel better! I've been admiring that chicken because it was like me. Now I want to be different, so I'm *glad* we're eating it!'

Later that evening, as Marcos went to his room to go to bed, he knelt on the floor and prayed. 'Lord Jesus, I'm sorry I've been such a big head. Help me to be nicer in future.' As he climbed between the sheets, he knew that God had heard him.

Lisbet goes to camp

Lisbet dangled her skinny legs over the edge of the iron bed frame, rubbed her eyes and yawned. The concrete floor felt cool to her bare feet as she groped for her second-hand school uniform and put it on. She didn't wash – there were no taps in her house. Only the dirty river three blocks away, and the lorry which came round selling water by the cylinder. Lisbet's family couldn't afford too much of that.

Idly, she wandered outside through the back door. The small yard had no plants, for no rain fell where they lived, and what water they had was too precious to water plants with. At one end was the toilet, a waist-high open cubicle enclosing a hole in the ground. The stench mingled with that of the acrid smoke from piles of burning rubbish in the road, but Lisbet was so used to it she hardly noticed.

Nearer the house was a rough shelter made of rush matting, enclosing an old kerosene stove and a few pots and pans. In another corner there was a large pile of discarded rusty tins which had once contained evaporated milk. Lisbet's father always maintained they might one day bring in some money, though the girl herself was never sure how. Three chickens were strutting around the yard, pecking at bits of rubbish. Nearly everyone kept chickens. They were useful for eggs, and for meat too, occasionally.

Her mother wasn't there. Lisbet knew she would have left the house in the early hours of the morning, for she spent each day selling fruit in the local street market, six blocks up the road. Her stall was a small affair, just a few piles of oranges on a cloth on the ground, surrounded by many other vendors, but she earned just enough to keep the family alive. Even so, Lisbet knew what it was to be hungry.

Her father came out to see if the hens had laid any eggs, and saw her. He was a good-looking man, despite the hardships of their existence. He was often away from home, however, for he had a few girl-friends in other parts. Lisbet was a little afraid of him, for sometimes he drank a lot, and then he would get angry, and shout, and beat her mother. He wasn't drunk now, but turned towards her impatiently.

'If it's breakfast you're wanting, forget it! Jose ate the last bread roll this morning and there's no money for more. Get off to school quickly, and hurry up and grow, so you can leave and earn some money for the family. What a waste of time sending girls to school!'

Lisbet knew her father was impatient because he was hungry himself, but even so, his words stung, and not for the first time. She knew he would not try to take her away from school. All the children in her area went to school. Everyone wanted to learn! And with several schools nearby it was so much easier than up in the mountains where she was born.

When she was just four years old, her family, together with hundreds of other families in that part of the

Andes, had decided to leave the high mountains and move down to the big city together, to invade a piece of waste land on the outer edge, and begin a new life. Life had been tough where they were, especially as the harvests had failed for two years in a row. Many had television sets and used to watch programmes about life in Lima, the capital city. If only they could live there, they'd be rich! they thought. There too would be the chance for their sons to study in school and university, and get good jobs. They made up their minds to go, and packed their bags.

That was four years ago. At first, they had only a few pieces of rush matting to make walls and a roof in which to live; the floor was just the dirty grey desert of that coastal region. They had been difficult days, adapting to the humidity and the constant cloud and mist over the coast for most of each year after the sunshine and thin, clear air of the mountains.

They had very soon discovered that most of the inhabitants of Lima were poor people like themselves, and not at all rich like those on the television screen. But they were a resourceful people, used to helping each other and working together. Lisbet's father came home with good news one day.

'Do you know what? That chap Miguel has bought an old car which he's going to use as a taxi. He wants someone to help him repair it. It's a bit battered, and we've not got all the spare parts we need, but it's amazing what you can do with a bit of string!'

'Do you mean he's offered you the job? That's tremendous!' Lisbet could remember her mother's sparkling eyes.

'Yes. We hope to open a garage eventually. So keep your eyes open for anything on the rubbish tips that might prove useful.'

And so Mrs Quispe had taken Lisbet and her young brother Jose over the local rubbish tips each day, searching not only for things for her husband, but also for bits of cardboard that they could sell for recycling. It was a bit smelly, delving into decaying cabbage leaves and dirty paper, and sometimes they were quite ill, but it helped bring in a bit more money and they were gradually able to build a more permanent home. It was still very basic, just bare concrete, first one wall, then another as the money came in, but it was a beginning. Others in their area were beginning to build, too. One day it would no longer be a rough shanty town, but a well-built suburb – but that was still a very long way off in the future.

After Lisbet had had her sixth birthday, she started school. Her mother then found the market job and used to take young Jose to spend the day with her. He used to enjoy being in the market. There were piles of mangoes, pineapples, guavas, coconuts and many other fruits grown mainly in the jungle area and transported in big lorries over the mountains and down to the coast. There were fresh vegetables and peppers, hunks of meat lying on wooden shelves, chickens squawking, waiting to be killed when a customer came, sheep's heads and all sorts of interesting bits of the insides of the animals. Best of all, there were fish. Lots of silvery, speckled fish, caught only that morning in the rich waters of the Pacific Ocean nearby.

'Want a banana?' someone's voice would call from a few metres away, and Jose would trot over and accept it gratefully. 'How's your big sister liking school?' the motherly woman would continue.

'She's all right,' Jose would murmur through a

mouthful of banana, before scampering quickly back to his mother's side.

He slept for a lot of the time, stretched out on the sacks around him. Lisbet would join them after school finished each day, and when she was old enough she helped her mother sell. Then Jose went to school, and another baby came along. Mother slung the little one in a shawl on her back and carried on as normal, feeding him there on the street, while she weighed out the fruit.

But one day, father had come home looking very glum. 'What's the matter?' asked his wife worriedly.

'It's Miguel. He's run into a spot of trouble with the police. They've put him in jail.' He sat down heavily onto a stool.

Mother stared at him. 'Then, what about your job?' she asked fearfully.

'That's gone, too, and he owes me two weeks' wages, as well! The scoundrel!'

Now there was no money to pay for extras. It was all they could do not to starve. When baby Lino became ill he very nearly died. But mother went begging from house to house in the evenings and so was able to buy him medicine.

Lisbet started off down the dusty road to school, her stomach rumbling and her mind churning over and over again what her father had said that morning. She knew a lot of people felt that way about girls. When a baby was born there were loud congratulations if it was a boy, polite good wishes if it was only a girl. And she couldn't help being only eight. Everyone took the same amount of time to grow up, didn't they? She couldn't hurry the days and years. And yet, Lisbet felt as if nobody wanted her. She was just a big nuisance to everybody. If she didn't have to go to school, she could at least help bring in some money, even if it meant rummaging in the rubbish again. She shuddered at the thought. But she *did* have to go to school, and, to be honest, it was better than staying at home, and she enjoyed learning.

Her thoughts turned to Sunday School the day before. That was good, too. There was a kind woman, called Anna, who had recently started the Sunday School in someone's house in the next road. Lots of children went. Anna came from a land far away called England, she knew, and she had come in a big aircraft to Peru so she could teach some people how to run Sunday Schools. Then they could teach boys and girls like her about Jesus. Lisbet didn't know very much about him yet, though her father often used his name, especially when he was angry.

She dimly remembered back in the village in the mountains watching great processions of people carrying an image of Jesus hanging dead on a cross. Everyone had been very sad. Sometimes people here in the city carried images of Mary or one of the saints. But in Sunday School, Anna spoke of Jesus being alive. Lisbet wondered at this.

Yesterday, Anna had come with some special news. 'How many of you have been to the beach?' she asked. The city was built right on the coast, but Lisbet had never seen the sea.

'We're going to have a camp in February,' Anna went on. 'We're going on a bus south of Lima to spend a few days and nights camping in tents together on the beach. There will be stories and games and things to do. It won't cost much, only. . . .'

Anna's voice had continued, but Lisbet felt cold inside. Her parents would never be able to afford the five pounds it would cost. She had looked around at the excited faces all around her. She could still see them in her mind, and remembered how most of them had started talking all at once, so Anna had to quieten them before she could go on explaining about it. But Lisbet remembered her mother's reaction, too, when she timidly mentioned the camp at home. Her mother had been sad more than angry.

'No, Lisbet, I'm sorry, but there's no way we can possibly afford it.'

The girl sighed as she thought about it now. But as she neared the school she met up with some of her classmates. She resolutely put her thoughts away and turned in at the gate with them.

Far away in England, a tall, fair-haired girl called Elizabeth ran home from church in her best dress, waving a letter at her mother.

'Mum! Read this. Can I go?'

'Lizzie, darling, can't you see I'm getting dinner? Come and stir the gravy while I find the carving knife for Daddy.'

Elizabeth obediently took the wooden spoon and stirred, having placed the letter on the sideboard out of the reach of both her young brother and the puppy. Her father began to carve the meat, whilst Mum dished out the Yorkshire pudding, roast potatoes and vegetables. But they were finishing their raspberry pavlova before Elizabeth spoke again about the letter.

'Mum, can I get my letter for you to read now?'

Her mother nodded. Elizabeth jumped up from her chair and thrust the piece of paper into her mother's hands.

'Please say I can do it!' she pleaded.

The letter was from Elizabeth's Sunday School teacher. It explained that their church's missionary in Peru, called Anna, had written about a camp she was hoping to lead for children from a shanty area of the capital, Lima, near where she lived and worked. Anna wrote about the needs of the children there and of the contrasts between the poor shanty towns and parts of the city centre with its beautiful architecture and modern shops. Elizabeth's teacher was writing to the parents of each of the children in her class, suggesting they might like to raise money to help really poor children go to that camp. They had thought of doing a sponsored walk to the town fourteen miles away.

'Well, my dear, as long as you're properly taken care of I don't see why you shouldn't do the walk. It would be good to help someone in need in another part of the world.'

Elizabeth gave her mother a hug, and actually volunteered to clear the table and stack the dishwashing machine!

The first day of February dawned hot and sticky again on the coast of Peru. It was high summer, with school holidays from January to March, the time of year when the clouds disappeared and the sun blazed down and made everyone sweat, even all night long. As Lisbet turned over on her thin mattress on the old, creaking bed-frame, she suddenly remembered. It was Sunday! And Anna had told her privately last week that there might be a nice surprise today! She thought wistfully of those going to camp the following week. Her father was still out of work, so there had been no change. Her parents just could not afford to let her go.

She dressed quickly, and ate the stale bread roll she

was offered with her sweet, black cinnamon tea. Then she left the house.

As she turned the corner, Lisbet heard Anna's yellow car bumping down the rough earth road. She and fifteen other children rushed eagerly to surround the vehicle as it came slowly to a halt. Thirty-two feet vied for a foothold on the bumpers. The children loved Anna, and she them.

'Hola! How are you? Nice to see you again – watch you don't hurt yourselves. Mind your fingers as I close the door!' Anna greeted them all happily, and most of the children darted ahead of her into the house where they would sing and pray, have quizzes and games, and learn about Jesus, their Friend. But Lisbet hung behind shyly.

'Anna, has the surprise come?' she whispered.

Anna took her hand, and told her some wonderful news. 'In England, the country where I come from, far away from Peru, some children have collected money to help with the camp. And one girl of about your age, with a name very like yours, wrote me a letter. You won't understand it, because it's written in English, but I'll tell you what it says. Look!'

Anna squatted down and showed Lisbet the letter. She read: 'I walked till my legs nearly dropped off, and I earned eight pounds. Please will you give it to a girl in your town, so she can go to camp?'

'I'd like to give it to you, Lisbet,' Anna told her with a smile. 'There's enough to pay for some food for your family, while you're away at camp, as well.'

Lisbet held the letter in her hand, hardly daring to believe what Anna had told her. She tried to say 'thank you' to Anna, but the words stuck in her throat. Suddenly she turned and squeezed her in a big hug, and then darted into the house.

The sand was warm under her bare toes, as Lisbet wriggled into a more comfortable position to listen to the story. Camp was even more wonderful than she'd imagined. She remembered again all that had happened so far. There had been that exciting bus journey, as they drove first through the city. Never had Lisbet seen such tall, magnificent buildings before, and so much hustle and bustle. She had knelt up on her seat and pressed her face to the window of the bus. They were in the main square, and there was the President's palace, guarded by special guards in white uniform with red trimmings, to match the flag that fluttered proudly from the roof.

'I like their boots!' she whispered to the girl in the seat next to hers. 'They're all black and shiny. And they've got things sticking out.'

'They're called spurs,' the girl replied. 'What I like is their helmets, with those lovely red plumes against the white.'

Lisbet gazed at the palace. What must it be like to live in such an enormous house, she wondered.

She rubbed her nose and pressed it to the window again, as they passed the end of a long road closed to traffic and full of shops. Could there really be so many shops in the world? Ow! She was getting pins and needles: better sit down again!

When Lisbet next knelt up to see out, she had a surprise. They were out of the city centre. Again she spoke to the girl. 'Look! Those houses are just like ours, but they're all painted blue!' They were perched on the desert hillside and looked attractive – from a distance!

With a shiver of excitement that tickled her all down

her back, Lisbet remembered how they had eventually passed through the city and were travelling down the Panamericana, the tarmacked main road that follows the coast of South America from Ecuador in the north to Chile in the south. The desert was on their left, but on their right lay the mighty Pacific Ocean. She had stared and stared. So this was the sea? So much water! Did it never end? She spent most of the time with her nose glued even more firmly to the window, watching the waves hungrily pounding the shore, or the flocks of pelicans and gulls which flew overhead. But from time to time she looked across the bus and out of the windows the other side.

Sometimes they passed through a river valley and Lisbet saw how the land around it was irrigated and a few crops grew. There were some chicken farms, too. She thought of the few chickens they had at home. What a lot of eggs these ones must produce! But most of the time, as the bus steadily ate up the kilometres, she saw just dry, dusty, often hilly earth on the left, and that vast expanse of water on the right.

Then suddenly the bus had slowed down and turned off the main road to the right, and everyone started cheering. There ahead of her, Lisbet could see several small, white tents, and one big one. As the vehicle slowed to a stop, she climbed off her seat and began to jump around in excitement. The other children did too! Anna and her helpers, mainly young people from her church, quickly organised the children.

'Come this way, Lisbet! Your tent is over here.' Lisbet skipped and jumped as she carried her small bag of spare clothes behind Anna.

The campsite lay between the sea and the road, and on the other side of the road was a track leading up to a farm where rice, sugar-cane and water melon grew. A neatly-made channel of water gushed down one side of the road at certain times of day, and from this pipes led into the fields to water the crops. Beyond the farm, the desert stretched away endlessly into the foothills of the Andes mountains.

Every day was a new adventure. They had lots of food to eat, until Lisbet thought she would burst! She'd never had so much in all her life before. Fancy having jam on her bread! Every morning there were chores to do.

'Grab the bucket – it's your turn, Lisbet!' someone called one morning, and Lisbet took the clanking pail up the sandy slope to the nearby water-pipe. While the water slowly trickled through she turned and watched the other children picking up litter and tidying the tents.

After the chores were done, Lisbet and the other children hurried into the big tent for some games and activities. What she liked best was making things with felt pens, scissors and glue. She'd never done that before! Next there was paddling in the sea. It took Lisbet two whole days to pluck up courage to do that. The sea played nasty tricks on you, like pretending to go away, and then coming up to splash you when you weren't expecting it! Lisbet was horrified when some of the children got knocked over by the waves, but they seemed to think it was fun, and their clothes soon dried off in the heat of the sun. Gradually Lisbet grew braver until she was splashing about with everyone else. It tasted nasty, though!

Anna had brought some special cream with her, to rub onto the children's bodies so they wouldn't burn. Her own skin was very fair, not like the children's beautiful brown bodies, and burnt even despite the cream.

In the late afternoon, when it wasn't quite so hot, they would all gather together and listen to a story from the Bible. Every day Lisbet learnt something new. She had made an important discovery in the past three days: that Jesus was her Friend, and cared about her. She felt so full of joy at first that she almost forgot how useless she felt usually. But as the time came towards returning home, that feeling came back. She hated the thought of leaving camp, where everyone had been so kind. But now it was story-time again, on the last afternoon of camp.

The summer sun shone down from a cloudless sky again that hot February afternoon, and the gulls were circling in their hundreds on the Pacific shoreline. Walter, one of the young men from the church, was telling a story. He was talking about the little man who climbed a tree in order to see Jesus better.

Lisbet's mind flitted to her old home in the mountains. There were trees there, tall eucalyptus trees. She'd almost forgotten them. She imagined Zacchaeus swarming up the thin trunk of one of those. She didn't know much about trees, really. There were hardly any where she lived now, on the desert coast.

Walter went on to talk about how God cared for everything he had made, even the little things, and how in nature he had made each creature to be important for all the rest in the chain of things. Each one was important, and God had made them in such a way that they were able to do all they had to do. Like the donkey and the llama, with their strong backs for carrying packs, or the tiny humming bird which was able to beat its wings so fast it could hover in one spot while it sucked nectar from the flowers.

Lisbet's gaze wandered. A tiny movement on the ground attracted her notice. An ant was crawling slowly over the sand about a metre away from her. Just one. She watched it, fascinated. The ground was crumbly, so it was no easy thing to climb over the grains of sand which must have seemed like boulders to the tiny ant. But even if it was difficult, the ant kept going. Lisbet turned once more to look at the story-teller.

'You see,' Walter was saying, 'your size makes no difference to your value. Zacchaeus was small, and the sort of person nobody noticed usually. They didn't even like him! But Jesus noticed him, and loved him, and made him feel wanted.'

Lisbet sat up straighter. Could it be true? That it didn't matter if other people thought she was small, and only a girl, and a bit of a nuisance, as long as Jesus didn't think like that?

Now Walter was saying something else. 'Jesus said that God cares so much that even if a little sparrow falls and dies, he notices. Then he said, "Don't be afraid, you are worth more than many sparrows." And again, to all the men and women and boys and girls who gathered to listen to him, Jesus said, "Look at the birds of the air; they do not sow or reap or store away in barns, and yet your heavenly Father feeds them. Are you not much more valuable than they?" '

Lisbet turned her eyes to the gulls, still wheeling and crying along the shoreline. God thought she was worth much more than they were.

Comforted in a way she could hardly describe to anyone else, she fell asleep quickly that night. Tomorrow she'd be going home, but she would have Jesus with her, her Friend, who valued her so much, and would help her to keep going in the difficult times.